The Personality Disorders

JAMES F. MASTERSON, M.D.

The Personality Disorders

A New Look at the Developmental Self and Object Relations Approach

Theory • Diagnosis • Treatment

ZEIG, TUCKER & CO., INC.
PHOENIX, ARIZONA

Published by

Zeig, Tucker & Co., Inc.
3618 North 24th Street
Phoenix, AZ 85016

Library of Congress Cataloging-in-Publication Data

Masterson, James F.
The personality disorders : a new look at the developmental self and object relations approach / James F. Masterson.
p. cm.
Includes bibliographical references and index.
ISBN 1-891944-33-9
1. Personality disorders. I. Title.
RC554.M274 1999 32777
616.85'8—DC21 CIP

Contents

Acknowledgments

First and foremost, I wish to thank my patients for their generosity in giving me permission to use their cases to help other therapists learn this approach. Their identities, of course, have been disguised.

I would like to thank my wife, Patricia, for her vital help at all stages in the preparation of this book, as well as with my previous books.

I would also like to thank Nancy Scanlan for her help not only with the manuscript for this book, but also with the manuscripts for all the other books going back to 1965.

I would like to thank Dorothy Kent for her help with the manuscript for the present book.

Finally, I would like to thank Suzi Tucker and Bernard Mazel for their professional guidance.

The Personality Disorders

Introduction

At the millennium, the diagnosis of personality disorder has evolved into one of the most important concepts in the field of psychotherapy. Patients considered untreatable 50 years ago are now able to remake their lives. However, it is also one of the youngest concepts—barely a half century old—and there is as yet no universally accepted consistent dynamic definition of the disorders and their treatment.

I have been intimately involved in this field for 40 years in research, teaching, and writing, and have been witness to and participant in the knowledge explosion that has occurred. Many of the ideas I initially presented 25 years ago have stood the test of time and remain valid today. Others have undergone evolution.

The aim of this book, written for psychotherapists, is to fill the need for a coherent, focused, and contemporary definition of the personality disorders. From the vantage point of the quarter-century mark, it reevaluates and updates the developmental self and object relations approach to the following issues.

1. The role of the mother or primary caretaker in the development of the normal self as viewed 25 years later.
2. The minimizing and denying of the role of the mother in the borderline personality disorder—25 years later.
3. The handicaps of the descriptive approach to diagnosis as presented in the fourth edition of the *Diagnostic and Statistical Manual of Mental Disorders* (DSM-IV) and the advantage of a psychodynamic approach.
4. The integrating influence of a concept of the self on an understanding of the personality disorders.
5. The use of intrapsychic structure to make a differential diagnosis among the personality disorders.

6. The differential diagnosis of those patients whose primary defense is focus on the object.
7. A complete report of a six-year course of successful psychoanalytic psychotherapy of a patient with a closet narcissistic defense against oedipal conflict that makes abundantly clear the differences in the content of working through between a preoedipal abandonment depression and a later oedipal conflict. A 19-month follow-up is also reported.
8. The diagnosis and treatment of intimacy problems in patients with personality disorders.

It addresses such questions as:

How have the views of the mother's role in the development of the normal self evolved in the last 25 years? What is the basis of Stern's and the attachment theorists' challenge to Mahler's theory? How does this challenge affect Mahler's theory and the clinical work based partially on it? Is her theory to be modified or discarded? How does the work of A. N. Schore on the neurobiology of the self contribute to this question? Which developmental theorist's perspective is appropriate for which personality disorder?

What is the importance of integrating the developmental role of the mother into the borderline patient's intrapsychic structure and the treatment? How do minimizing and denying the mother's role affect other therapists' treatment approaches? How does my point of view compare with the work of Kernberg, Kohut, Adler, Gunderson, Meissner? Is Linehan's DBT therapy indicated for all borderline patients or only for lower-level patients?

What are the assets and handicaps of the DSM-IV system and how does it compare with a psychodynamic approach? How does the concept of the self contribute to an understanding of the personality disorders? How does one differentiate among a closet narcissistic personality disorder, a schizoid personality disorder, and a distancing borderline personality disorder?

The lower-level psychotic border of the personality disorders seems quite clear, but the upper-level neurotic border remains a problem—so much so that many personality-disordered patients, particularly if they function well, are diagnosed as psychoneurotic, and receive classical analytic treatment, which does not touch the core of their disorder. Three chapters present a complete report of six years of psychoanalytic psychotherapy of a closet narcissistic personality disorder defense against a neurosis, illustrating clearly the differences in clinical content of the working-through phase of a preoedipal abandonment depression and an oedipal castration conflict. In addition, a 19-month follow-up is reported.

The last chapter addresses the following: What are the illusions of intimacy in the personality disorders? How does the therapist decode these illusions and help the patient to identify his or her defenses against abandonment and/or engulfment and bring the patient to work through these painful affects and overcome his or her vulnerability to intimacy.

Part I

Theory

Chapter One

The Role of the Mother or Primary Caretaker in the Development of the Normal Self

25 Years Later

Twenty-five years ago I published a report[1.29] citing the mother's difficulty in supporting the child's emerging self as an etiologic agent in the borderline personality disorder. This view was based on clinical research with patients, but relied heavily on Mahler's[1.20–1.25] theory of the important role of the mother in the normal development of individuation and the sense of self.

In recent years, Mahler's theory has been challenged by later researchers, such as Stern[1.39] and the attachment researchers,[1.14] suggesting that Mahler may have studied infants with insecure attachment rather than normals, and yet Mahler's theory continues to be useful to the psychoanalytic psychotherapy of the personality disorders (disorders of the self). Beyond that, the importance of genetic vulnerabilities and neurobiology has come to the fore.[1.36]

This chapter reviews the developmental theories of Mahler,[1.20–1.25] Stern,[1.39] the attachment researchers,[1.14] and Schore.[1.36] It focuses on the role of the mother and the mother–child interaction in an attempt to resolve this contradiction. In addition, it compares and contrasts these theories, particularly with regard to their usefulness in the psychoanalytic psychotherapy of the personality disorders (disorders of the self).

REVIEW OF MAHLER'S STUDY OF THE SEPARATION–INDIVIDUATION PROCESS

Mahler[1.20–1.25] studied what she called the normal separation–individuation process by direct observation of infants from 2½ months of age to their 31st month to determine how a child achieves a separate sense of self while functioning in the presence of the mother: an intrapsychic sense of separateness of self from the mother, an independent identity.

Theory

Mahler[1.17–1.25] conceived of the separation–individuation process as two complementary developments: separation consists of the child's emergence from the symbiotic fusion with the mother, and individuation consists of those achievements that mark the child's assumption of his or her own individual characteristics.

Mahler reported[1.17–1.25]: "Even those children with the sturdiest constitution can become psychotic when subjected to severe staggering traumatization during the vulnerable autistic or symbiotic phases of development, whereas in those with the weakest nature or constitution, nurture does not suffice to overcome their innate defects."

She stressed that the capacity for individuation was an innate given, but she also viewed the infant as a passive receptor—a view common at the time—rather than as a cocreator of this process.

She also stressed that "the specific unconscious need of the mother activated out of the infinite potentials of the child those in particular that create for each mother 'the child' who reflects her own unique individual needs." This process takes place, of course, within the range of the child's innate dominance. Mutual cueing during the symbiotic phase creates that indelibly imprinted configuration, that complex pattern that becomes the motif for the infant's becoming the child of this particular mother. In other words, the mother conveys in normal ways a kind of mirroring reference to which the infant automatically adjusts.

She continued, pointing out that if the mother's primary preoccupation with her infant, her mirroring function, is unpredictable, unstable, anxiety ridden, or hostile, then the individuating child has to do without a reliable frame of reference for checking back perceptually and emotionally. The result will be disturbance in the primitive self field.

Clinical Research[1.17–1.25]

It is important to keep in mind that this was a pioneer effort by a psychoanalyst who was deeply embedded in psychoanalytic theory. Mahler[1.18, 1.19] came to this work with an already-present conviction about the "normal" developmental process of symbiosis and separation–individuation derived from her study of symbiotic child psychosis, which, she believed, was a result of the greatest deviation of the normal symbiotic phase and the complete failure of separation–individuation.

A comparison study of average mothers and their normal babies was needed to substantiate the universality of the hypothesis. Mahler set out to "prove" her assumptions, not to discover what went on. The idea of "fusion with the mother" came from work with child schizophrenia and infantile psychosis.

After a preliminary pilot study between 1959 and 1962 in which 17 children of 16 mothers were studied, the formal research study began in January 1962 and lasted until June 1968; it consisted of 21 children of 13 mothers, 12 boys and nine girls. The average age of entry into the study was 2½ months, and the range of entry was one week to 10 months. The average age at termination was 31 months. The average age of the mothers was 31, and the average age of the fathers was 36.

Inferences were made from observation of an infant's behavior as to the infant's intrapsychic life. The observational process was extensive, with participant observations once or twice per week for each mother–child pair (dual unity). There were also weekly interviews with the mother, once- or twice-yearly interviews with the father, filming according to a chronological guideline, and home visits of approximately one to three hours every other month.

The children received developmental psychological tests at least four times: at 5, 10, 18, and 30 months, and in addition, the toddlers had play sessions. The mothers had an initial psychological evaluation.

The Research Study[1.20–1.25]

It is important also to emphasize that the focus was on the infants' development from 4 to 5 months of age on, so that the autistic and symbiotic phases were derived not from actual study of the infants, but from the study of infantile psychotics, the results of which were theorized to occur in normals.

Autistic Stage (0–2 Months)

Mahler derived this stage mostly from psychoanalytic theory applied to a study of infantile psychotics, and since it was highly theoretically influenced, it will be very briefly summarized. The infant in a state of normal autism seems to be in a state of primitive hallucinatory disorientation in which the need for satisfaction seems to belong to his or her own "unconditional" omnipotent autistic orbit. The task of this phase is the achievement of homeostatic equilibrium in the extramural environment. There is a stimulus barrier that protects the infant's psyche from being overwhelmed. This leads to the symbiotic stage.

Symbiotic Stage (2–4 Months)

From the second month on, a dim awareness of the need for a satisfying object marks the beginning stage of normal symbiosis, in which the infant behaves and functions as if he or she and the mother were an omnipotent system—a dual unity within one common boundary. The essential feature of the symbiosis is hallucinatory, delusional somatopsychic omnipotent fusion with a representation of the mother, and, in particular, the delusion of a common boundary between two physically separate individuals.

It is within the matrix of this physiological and sociobiological dependence on the mother that the structural differentiation takes place that leads to the individual's organization for adaptation, functioning self, and ego. But in the symbiotic stage, there is not yet a differentiation of inner from outer or of self from other. The investment of the mother is the principal psychological achievement of this stage. The symbiotic organizers of this psychological birth are the mother's holding behaviors.

Separation-Individuation Stage (5–30 Months)

The First Subphase—Differentiation and Development of the Body Image (3–8 Months)

Mahler noted that the child's attention shifts to the perceptual conscious system, which enables the infant to have a more permanently alert sensorium whenever he or she is awake. This is seen in a look of much greater alertness, persistence, and goal directedness. His or her attention gradually expands into one that is outwardly directed to perceptual activity. The mother's preferred soothing pattern is taken over and assimilated by the infant in his or her own way. The baby begins to compare the mother with others. At about 8 months of age, the child develops stranger anxiety, but it is as much curiosity as it is anxiety.

The Second Subphase—Practicing (10–15 Months)

The practicing subphase is divided into two further subphrases: early and proper. Early, the baby crawls using the mother as a stable base, but has more pleasure in his or her own ego apparatus and tends to refuel with mother.

Then, with the acquisition of cognition and upright locomotion (the ability to walk), the child enters the emotional state of the "love affair with the world," with great emphasis on practicing and mastering his or her own skills and autonomous function. There is a relative imperviousness to knocks and falls and other frustrations. The child is enamored with the world and his or her own grandeur and omnipotence. There is a relative obliviousness to the presence of the mother.

In the very next month following active free locomotion, great strides are made toward asserting individuality. This seems to be the first giant step toward identity formation.

The Third Subphase—Rapprochement (15–22 Months)

With the growth of cognitive facilities and increasing differentiation of the sense of separateness, there is also a noticeable waning of the child's previous imperviousness to frustration, as well as a diminishing of what has been a relative obliviousness to his or her mother's presence. Increased separation anxiety can be observed, reflected in shadowing of the mother and darting away. As the toddler's awareness of separation grows, the child seems to have an increased need or a wish for the mother's response.

This underlines the importance of the mother's optimal emotional availability or attuning to the subphase. A symbiotic language, as well as other types of intercommunication, come into play and become increasingly prominent. The toddler must gradually and painfully give up the delusion of his or her own grandiosity, often by way of dramatic fights with the mother. This is what is termed the rapprochement crisis—the child wishes to retain his or her grandiosity and, at the same time, have the mother fulfill all needs. So the mood shifts to dissatisfaction and irritability and an ambitendency toward the mother. Affects may range widely, with much irritability, and object permanence is also established. In addition, at this time, the child moves to an active extension of the mother–child world, primarily to include the father, but also others.

Rapprochement Crisis

At around 18 months, a conflict arises in which the toddler seems to have a desire to be separate, grand, and omnipotent, on the one hand, and, on the other, to have the mother magically fulfill his or her wishes without having to recognize that the help is actually coming from the outside from the other. Thus the mood shifts to one of general dissatisfaction and insatiability; the infant tends to use the mother as an extension of the self, denying the painful awareness of separation.

Resolution of Crisis

The establishment of object permanency—in other words, the ability to realize that the mother could be elsewhere and could be found—is now well established and helps to reassure the toddler who is experiencing the emotion of missing the mother. Some children came to use transitional phenomena to deal with this. As each child found the optimal distance from the mother, the clamoring for omnipotent control, extreme periods of separation anxiety, and the alternation of demands for closeness and autonomy subsided.

The Fourth Subphase—Consolidation of individuation and the Beginning of Object Constancy (22–30 Months)

Here object constancy becomes fluid and reversible. There is an unfolding of complex cognitive functions and verbal communication, the establishment of separate mental representations of the self and the object, the development of fantasy and reality testing: the boy's awareness of his penis and reliance on his own body and motor activity to push him forward; the girl's feelings of hurt and anger at her mother, her becoming more prone to depression.

Comment

Mahler's work has been challenged by Stern and the attachment researchers. This will be considered in the discussion after their work has been reviewed.

INTERPERSONAL WORLD OF THE INFANT: A REVIEW OF DANIEL STERN'S VIEW OF INFANT DEVELOPMENT

The first stage of observation of the development of normal children emerged in the 1950s and 1960s, introduced by Spitz,[1.38] Escalona,[1.10] Mahler,[1.17] Bowlby,[1.3] and others, and their work contributed greatly to our perception and understanding of clinical phenomena. A second stage of infant researchers (D. Stern,[1.39] T. Brazelton,[1.4, 1.5] R. Emde,[1.7, 1.8] and others) appeared in the 1970s and, aided by more advanced research methods, have gone beyond observation to experimentation. The results have called into question many of the psychoanalytic theories of development. The following briefly reviews the research.

Like Mahler, Stern[1.39] draws conclusions regarding the child's intrapsychic state from observing the child's behavior. Stern's work thus must be viewed as an invention—a working hypothesis regarding the infant's subjective experience of his or her own social life. It is a report not only of his own work, but of many others, including developmental psychologists in the burgeoning field of infant research. However, the work by Stern and the others was based more on experiment than on simple observation. And they approached it with a greater inclination to study what went on rather than to prove a hypothesis.

The essential findings can be summarized as follows:

1. The infant is predesigned to be perceptually separate from birth, with a fully active perceptual apparatus that seeks to organize his or her affective experience with reality.
2. There is a very active dialogue between infant and self-regulating object from the beginning. The infant is a co-creator of his or her own development.
3. There is no stimulus barrier, undifferentiated phase, or autistic or symbiotic phase.
4. Self and self-regulating object representations mature in parallel from the beginning.
5. Orality is not the special vehicle for internalization. All perceptual modes participate in internalization.
6. Id and the pleasure principle do not precede ego and the reality principle—a simultaneous dialectic evolves from the beginning of life.
7. Basic domains of human connection evolve from the infant's active construction of representations of interactions with self-regulating others.
8. There are four senses of self: emergent, core, intersubjective, verbal.
9. Senses of self are the primary organizer; there are sensitive periods, but all exist throughout life. Such issues as dependency and autonomy are not phase specific, but are life-course issues.
10. The sharing of interpersonal experience or mental states creates "attunements" crucial to the growth of the self.
11. Selective attunement potently shapes the development of the child's subjective and intrapsychic life—that is, the infant becomes the child of his or her particular mother.

The exact import of all this new information will have to be replicated and validated by further research and the test of time, but it has opened new and exciting avenues of exploration.

The Stages of the Self[1,39]

The Emerging Self (0–2 Months)

The basic feelings of human connectedness evolve from the infant's active construction of representations of interactions with self-regulating others. The infant cocreates the sense of self and the sense of the object. When the infant's early diverse experiences are linked or connected, the infant experiences the emergence of organization. The first such organization concerns the body: its coherence, its actions, its inner feelings, and the memory of all these. The sense of the emerging self thus concerns the process and product of forming organization and learning about the relationships among the infant's separate experiences.

Infants are predesigned to be able to perform a cross-modal transfer of information that permits a correspondence across all perceptual modalities—touch, vision, and so on. Thus is formed the emerging sense of self.

The Core Self (2–6 Months)

In this stage, the infant forms a sense of a core self and core others. The experiences available to the infant to form an organized sense of a core self and others include:

1. Self-agency
2. Self-coherence
3. Self-activity
4. Sense of continuity

These take place completely outside of awareness. This sense of self is experiential, not cognitive. At this time, it is important to keep in mind that the infant is able to see perceptually, but not emotionally, that the mother is separate. At the same time, he or she experiences the mother's caretaking ministrations as being part of himself or herself. Most likely, memory helps to integrate agency coherence affectivity and continuity into an organizing subjective perspective.

Episodes of memory are organized into "rigs" or representations of interactions that have been generalized. These rigs thus constitute a representation of the core self and others. At this stage, the infant's own experience is regulated by self-regulating others. From 2 to 7 months, an enormous sector of the entire affective spectrum of the infant's field is possible only in the presence of, and with the interactive mediation of, the mother, including the regulation of attention, curiosity, cognition. However, the infant registers the objective experience with self-regulating others as a subjective experience. Stern stressed that the infant has the capacity for evocative memory as early as 3 months, whereas the usual age for memory recall as reported by others is 9 to 12 months.

Intersubjective Self (7–15 Months)

The next quantitative leap in the sense of self occurs when the infant discovers, between the seventh and ninth month, that he or she functions mentally and that other people have minds as well, and that others can have a mental state similar to or different from that of the infant. At this point, the interpersonal action moves from overt actions to internal subjective states behind those actions. The self becomes aware of the process of empathy. The issue of what kind of self experiences are to be shared arises. Intersubjectivity is not just a matter of separation of the self from the child's view of the mother, but one that fosters the development of a more complex relationship with the mother, as well as a more autonomous sense of self. This discovery amounts to the child's discovering a "theory" of separate but interfaceable minds.

Core relatedness, with its establishment of the physical and sensory distinctions of self and other, is a necessary precondition for the development of a subjective self that involves sharing, since the possibility of sharing has no meaning unless it was a transaction that reflects the surety of the physically distinct separate self and other.

The sense of subjective self brings up the issue of how affects are to be shared, or affect attunement. The sharing of affective states is the most pervasive feature of the intersubjective sense of self.

The Verbal Self (15–30 Months)

During the second year, the infant's acquisition of language provides a new medium of exchange to create shared meanings; it permits the child to begin to construct a narrative of his or her own life. Symbolic play and language now become possible: children can conceive of, and then refer to, themselves as external or objective entities. Self-reflection becomes possible; since the self can now be considered an objective entity. Language not only increases sharing, but also inhibits the preverbal domains of experience. For the first time, the self can have a wish as to how reality ought to be, contrary to fact. Meaning now results from interpersonal negotiations about what can be agreed upon as shared.

Language recasts and transforms experiences of core and intersubjective relatedness so that it fractures experience. Language forces a space between interpersonal experience as lived and as represented. Language and symbolic thinking give the child tools with which to distort reality. They can create expectations contrary to past experience. In fact, everything learned is the by-product of uniting two mentalities in the common symbol system or the forging of shared meaning.

Language does not just promote individuation, but also achieves the next developmental level of relationship with the object at which all existential life situations will then be played out. It does bring about the ability to narrate one's own life story, with all the potential it holds. With the advent of language, some behaviors now have a privileged status with regard to one's having to own them. Thus, many messages or many channels are being fragmented by language into a hierarchy of accountability and deniability.

Clinical Comment

Stern reported not only the results of his own work on early development, but also that of many others. The child-observation research advanced by leaps and bounds throughout the 1970s and 1980s, following Mahler's work in the 1950s and 1960s. Stern emphasized that the child's stages of development occur much earlier than reported by Mahler since they were studied at a much earlier time in the child's life. He does make the important point that the child is "prewired" at birth to be separate from the mother and to be an extremely active partner in the cocreation of his or her sense of self and inner objects. Although Stern contradicted Mahler's notion of autism symbiosis and the need for the separation of the self from the object, there is a dramatic change in the child's perception of the caretaking object as the child moves from the core self to the intersubjective self. In the former, he or she perceives the mother simply as a physical object, like any other object, and experiences her caretaking activities as part of himself or herself. In the intersubjective stage, the child sees the mother as a person with a separate need resembling his or her own. In the stage of the core self, the child perceptually sees the mother as separate but emotionally experiences her actions as part of the self, so there is not an emotional separation.

Stern[1.39] minimized this lack of an emotional separation and presented a contradiction when he said that the other is still perceived as a separate core. How can the child perceive the other as separate and still not perceive that the actions come from the other? If the child cannot do this emotionally, there has to be a lack of emotional separateness. Perhaps Stern took this view to contrast his view from Mahler's. Beyond that, Stern did not cite locomotion as important, and splitting was not a likely experience of infants as observed, but the product of a postinfancy mind.

ATTACHMENT RESEARCHERS: BOWLBY AND HIS FOLLOWERS (AINSWORTH, MAIN, SOLOMON, ET. AL.)

Bowlby[1.3] designed a model of emotional development that was free of drive theory and was based on observable behavior that could be scientifically validated rather than used to infer what was going on in the child's mind. This differentiates his approach from that of Mahler and Stern.

Bowlby's work began with James Robertson's[1.32] observations from 1948 through 1952, at the Hampstead Nursery, of children between the ages of 18 months and 4 years who either had gone to a residential nursery or to a hospital for weeks or months and then returned home. Bowlby combined Robertson's observations with those of a research project by Heinicke[1.11] on brief separations and with a number of other cross-cultural studies to propose some powerful postulates from observations of the behavior of children in their second and third years of life when separated from their mothers by stays in residential nurseries or hospital wards and cared for in traditional ways and then returned home.

Once the child is over the age of 6 months, he or she tends to respond to separation as follows: (a) Protest and wish for reunion. This may begin immediately or be delayed. It lasts from a few hours to a week or more. (b) Despair, which succeeds protest. The child is preoccupied with the missing mother and seems to feel increasing hopelessness. (c) Detachment sooner or later succeeds protest and despair if the mother does not return.

Should the child's stay in the hospital be prolonged and he or she be exposed to the experience of being attached to a series of nurses, each of whom leaves and so repeats for him the experience of the original loss of his mother, he or she will in time act as if neither mothering nor contact with humans has much significance.

A variable that was found regularly to be associated with increased disturbance both during separation and after return was the length of the separation.[1.11] There is no evidence that only those children whose relationship with the mother was unfavorable prior to the separation were distressed by the separation. The more affectionate the relationship, the greater is the child's upset during separation. Whatever part is played by other variables in determining separation distress, by far the most weighty is the loss by a child of his or her mother.

Mahler assumed that the infant begins in a symbiotic relationship with the mother, so she focused on separation from the mother, whereas Bowlby, following Sander,[1.33–1.35] studied the task of focusing on the mother from 9 to 18 months: the infant's efforts to gain physical access to the primary caregiver as a source of comfort and safety and as a social and emotional partner, which Bowlby equates to secure attachment. Bowlby divided attachment into secure and insecure.

Bowlby turned to ethology theory (see Heinicke and Westheimer[1.11]) to postulate that all infants possess a basic instinct of attachment to caretakers and adapt their interpersonal behaviors in ways that assure them of adequate caregiver availability and responsiveness.

In 1970 Ainsworth,[1.1] following Bowlby's theory, carried out a pioneering study of the organization of infant attachment patterns into secure (60% to 70% American families) and insecure. The insecure were further divided into avoidant, resistant, and disoriented/disorganized. These patterns have been repeatedly described by many attachment researchers.[1.26–1.28]

In the infants with secure attachment, they did not find in the practicing phase the unawareness of the mother that Mahler described, nor did they find the ambivalence Mahler described in the rapprochement phase. However, they did find these phenomena in the children with insecure attachment.

A second generation of researchers[1.26–1.28] examined the attachment problems beyond the first year of children of mothers who were depressed, bipolar, alcoholic, or maltreating, and they found all three insecure patterns as follows:

The avoidant: The mothers were covertly rejecting, the infant was not upset at separation and avoided the mother on her return. *The resistant*: This was a much smaller number. These mothers were more disengaged and less responsive and the children showed alternate clinging and resistance. *The disorganized/disoriented*: The mothers were bipolar or depressed, alcoholic or abusive, or neglectful. The infants were not able to organize any consistent strategy for organizing approach-avoidance behavior to deal with discomfort under stress, therefore, they are called disorganized/disoriented.

Modern Attachment Theorists and Mahler[1.14]

The attachment researchers,[1.1, 1.2, 1.9, 1.13–1.16, 1.30] following up on the infants to ages 10 to 24 months and thereby observing them during Mahler's rapprochement stage, were not able to confirm Mahler's observation that the normal infant goes through a stage of ambivalence. In other words, harmonious interaction and absence of ambivalence during reunions were the predominant pattern of behavior from 20 months of age, and probably beyond. Beyond that, they found that the ambivalent behaviors only occurred in the minority of infants in less positive caregiving relationships.

"Longitudinal observations suggest that these insecure attachment patterns by these infants toward their mothers at 18 months is part of a more deep-seated disturbance of the caregiving relationship present early in the first year and rooted in characteristic defensive responses of the mother that involved difficulties with the affect of engagement and effective comforting and soothing of the infant at times of stress."[1.14]

It was found that the children who had the best adjustment at 24 months of age[1.9, 1.13–1.16, 1.30] were those who at 12 to 18 months of age showed secure attachment responses that often included distress at separation. Hence these children appeared less autonomous in the absence of the parent. It turned out that those who were upset at separation and able to seek out the parent showed the more adaptive development at the age of 24 months. Could what Mahler viewed as autonomy have been defensive distancing?

The researchers concluded that children who went through ambivalence in the rapprochement stage were not normal but more likely suffered from pathology that had been in place in the mother–child relationship during the first year of life. As a matter of fact, those children whose earlier relationship with the mother was positive managed the rapprochement stage without ambivalence.

The quality of give-and-take within the caregiving relationship—particularly the toddler's ability to integrate his or her initiatives into social give-and-take while maintaining warm relatedness—is likely to be a better indication of the toddler's function than is his or her independent behavior of any kind at all. Assertive relatedness rather than autonomy better describes adaptive behavior in toddlerhood.[1.14] Finally, grandiosity and the splitting defense are not a part of normal development, but a part of pathological development.

The attachment researchers confirm Mahler's notion of the importance of the mother to the emergence of the self. However, they stress the different pathway that this takes in the child.

Comment

Researchers have concluded that the organization of normal states of the infant–mother relationship is very different from the pathological, and that a theory of normal development is needed that is not based on retrospective analyses of pathological states. There is also a need for a theory of psychopathology not based on the fixation of normal states, since the normal and the pathological develop so differently.[1.14]

AFFECT REGULATION AND THE ORIGIN OF THE SELF: A. N. SCHORE

An exciting and profoundly important more recent contribution to our understanding of the role of the mother in the development of the child's self comes not from the psychoanalytic study of children such as those by Mahler, Stern, and Bowlby, but from the world of neurobiological research as reported by A. N. Schore.[1.36]

I have attempted here only to abstract and summarize some of his perspectives. The reader is strongly urged to read the book itself to grasp the depth and complexity of his contribution.

Infant studies, animal research, and studies from developmental neuroanatomy and neurochemistry have found that neurobiological development is interactive. Development essentially represents a number of sequential mutually driven infant caregiver processes that occur in a continuing dialectic between a maturing organism and the changing environment. It now appears that affect is what is actually transacted within the mother–infant dyad, and this highly efficient system of emotional communication is essentially nonverbal. Human development cannot be understood apart from this affect-transacting relationship.

The mother, the primary social object, mediates the physical environment of the infant. The mother's modulatory function is essential, not only to every aspect of the infant's current functioning, but also for the child's continuing development. She is thus the major source of environmental stimulation that facilitates or inhibits the experience-dependent maturation of the child's developing neurobiological structures. Her essential role as the psychobiological regulator of the child's immature psychophysiological systems directly influences the child's biochemical growth processes that support the genesis of new structures.

Findings

In the first years of postnatal life, the brain grows two and one-half times its size at birth. This human brain growth spurt is at least five-sixths postnatal, and continues until about 18 to 24 months of age. During this postnatal period, those brain regions in which the most rapid growth takes place are most susceptible or sensitive to external stimulation. Late-maturing cortical areas that differentiate after subcortical brain-stem areas are particularly sensitive to postnatal influence. Higher cortical levels come to inhibit earlier-developing lower subcortical levels.

Thus the major part of the development of the axons, dendrites, and synaptic connections that underlie all behavior is known to take place in early and late infancy. The growth of dendrites and synapses is experience sensitive and experience dependent, but the exact nature of such experience is still only vaguely defined. However, it is clear that the primary caregiver is the most important source.

The maturation of the prefrontal cortex occurs in the last quarter of the first year of infancy, and makes interconnections that are affected by environmental stimuli during the critical period, which then become firmer.

Dr. Schore's Theory

A center for the control of affect, motivation, and social functioning emerges in the first year of life in the right orbital prefrontal cortex. This happens during a developmental stage that begins at the end of the first year and ends in the middle of the second year. This late-maturing higher cortical structure is situated at the apex of the limbic system and its extensive cortical connections and the hierarchical dominance of the lower subcortical limbic structures account for its preeminent role in socioemotional functioning.

It has been found that the expression of genetic influences requires transactions with the environment during sensitive periods. Maternal behavior itself is thought to be an external environmental event that mediates genetic differences.

The author suggests that the practicing stage, roughly between 10 and 18 months of age, is a critical period for the development of social–

emotional function. At the end of the first year, increased and more efficient attachment functioning between the mother and child is associated with the appearance of high levels of positive affect that characterize the early practicing period, roughly between 10 and 12 months of age. These events, in turn, directly influence the growth of connections between cortical and limbic structures in the infant's developing brain that are associated with attachment function. A significant change in dyadic affective transactions occurring in the late practicing period accounts for further maturation of these structures. The intervals between 10 to 12 months and 16 to 18 months are critical periods for the final maturation of the system in the prefrontal cortex that is essential to the regulation of affect over the rest of the life span.

At birth, the human is remarkably ill equipped to cope with the variations and excitations of the environment. He or she is a subcortical creature that is in danger of going into shock through overreacting to powerful or unexpected stimuli because of the lack of a means for modulating behavior that is made possible by the development of cortical control. The role of the higher structures is played by the mother. She is the child's auxiliary cortex.

Of special importance is late dyadic transactions with the mother in which she regulates the infant's affective state in the short term, which leads to structural change over the long term. Secure attachment facilitates the transfer of regulatory capacities from caregiver to infant. It is the mother's external regulation of the infant's developing immature emotional systems during particular critical periods of brain differentiation that is the essential factor that influences the *experience-dependent* growth of brain areas prospectively involved in self-regulation. This growth takes place in stages, and at the end of each stage, a more complex structure is capable of a more complex regulatory function. The outcome of effective dyadic affect regulatory transactions is an integration and restructuring of the infant's developing socioemotional regulatory system.

This center's connection with hypothalamic and autonomic areas, as well as brain-stem neuromodulator systems, plays an essential adaptive role in emotional and motivational processes. At the orbital frontal level, cortically processed exteroceptive information concerning the external environment is integrated with subcortically processed interoceptive information regarding the visceral endocrine environment. This prefrontal autonomic control is responsible for the visceral interoceptive "gut feelings" that are experienced in its response to both real and imagined threats.

There are neural anatomic connections between the orbital frontal cortex center and the limbic system. This is a site of convergence of limbic and autonomic connections. A theory is proposed that there are two limbic forebrain and midbrain circuits, one associated with a dopaminergic ventral tegmental area and the other with the noradrenergic lateral tegmental area. The author speculates that these two structural systems are associated with respective dual excitatory and inhibitory functional mechanisms of the limbic system. The ventral tegmental circuit with dopaminergic neurons in the midbrain represents an energy-expending component of the sympathetic nervous system. A lateral tegmental circuit that originates in noradrenergic neurons in the medulla and courses along the ventral noradrenergic bundle represents an energy-conserving component of the parasympathetic nervous system. Ventral tegmental event: dopaminergic–sympathic system–energy expanding. Lateral tegmental event: noradrenergic–parasympathetic–energy conserving.

The Author's Theory of Regulation of Affect and Social Interaction

It is hypothesized that the maturation center in the prefrontal cortex originates in the specific critical period at the end of the first year of life (10 to 12 months) and that maternal regulated high-intensity stimulation provided at this time through psychobiologically attuned, arousal-amplyfing reciprocal gaze transactions generates and sustains positive affect in the dyad. These transactions induce particular neuroendocrine changes that facilitate the expansion and innervation of deep sites in the orbital frontal areas of the right hemisphere, as well as ascending subcortical areas of the neurochemical circuit of the limbic system—the sympathetic ventral tegmental limbic circuit. This imprinting experience initiates the maturation of a frontal limbic excitatory system that is responsible for the developmental adaptations in the beginning phase of the practicing period—behavioral hyperactivity, high levels of positive affective play behavior, and subsequently the establishment of the capacity to form an interactive representational model that underlies an early functional system of affect regulation.

The second significant change occurs in the second year with the onset of socialization. The 14- to 16-month-old infant's response to such stressful socialization transactions is frequently a state of hypoarousal. These stage-typical stress states, accompanied by a different pattern of psychoneuroendocrine alterations, serve as an optimal social stimulus for the expansion of the other limbic circuit, the parasympathetic lateral tegmental limbic circuit. The experience-dependent wiring of this circuit into the orbital frontal cortex allows for the emergence of an efficient and adaptive inhibitory system. The competition between the sympathetic and parasympathetic limbic circuits underlies a parcellation process that produces a mature differentiated orbital frontal system at about 18 months, the end of the critical period.

Comment

Schore's theory, which needs further validation, opens the door to an understanding of the neurological wiring that underlies the development of the self. He makes clear that in his view there is a neurobiological symbiosis between the mother and child that is a requisite for the development and structuring of the center in the orbital frontal cortex.

DISCUSSION: CHALLENGES TO MAHLER'S THEORY

Mahler's work, which opened the door to the development of psychoanalytic psychotherapy of the personality disorders, has been challenged by the work of Stern and the attachment researchers. Stern found that the infant is prewired to see the mother as separate from birth, that is, there is no autistic or symbiotic phase. The attachment researchers found no unawareness of the mother in the practicing phase and no ambivalence in the rapprochement phase. None of these researchers found any developmental grandiosity or developmental splitting defenses. The grandiosity seen in patients presumably must arise from identification with the parent.

The attachment researchers suggested that Mahler was studying infants with insecure attachment, not secure attachment. How are we to resolve the apparent paradox that a theory that has been and remains so clinically useful is not what it appears to be? Was Mahler studying infants with secure or insecure attachment? Some information on this issue can be found by reviewing Mahler's reports of the mother's response to the child's individuation during the symbiotic phase and from two follow-up reports on three of the infants by Bergman and Fahey and McDevitt.[1.31]

The children were "normally endowed," but the criteria for the selection of these children are not clear, and they were only 2½ to 10 months old when selected. Although the mothers were studied as part of the dual unit and were also given Rorschach tests, there are no reports of the mothers' personalities and backgrounds, and there are a number of descriptions of mother–child interactions that themselves suggest that the mothers may have had pathological attitudes toward their children's individuation (see Mahler et al.,[1.17] pp. 58–62, 68–70). Eleven of 13 mothers showed pathological attitudes toward their children's separation–individuation during the stage of symbiosis, sounding far more like mothers with personality disorders than healthy mothers, and the behavior of 10 of the children seems to show avoidant attachment.

Bergman and Fahey, as well as McDevitt,[1.31] are following up 15 of the 21 children to adulthood (ages 25 to 30). At this point, only three who provide clinical material relevant to this inquiry have been reported.

Bergman and Fahey reported on two of the children as follows:

The first child's mother had had difficulty with her own mother, with whom she longed for closeness. She clung to her daughter, idealized her, and felt rejected by her growth. The daughter showed a good capacity for individuation but an insecure attachment, alternately clinging and resisting. She seemed to adapt in adult life through one-to-one relationships at work and with her husband.

Impression: Sounds like a borderline mother and a borderline child who adapts well when her defenses are reinforced.

The second child's mother had difficulty mothering, and longed for the unconditional love of her daughter that she didn't get from her own mother. The mother focused more on her own needs that on her daughter's, tended to withdraw when the daughter was in crisis, and felt rejected when her daughter's attention was elsewhere. The daughter's relationship was insecure attachment, alternately clinging and resisting, and she developed constipation from battles over toilet training that still persists. As an adult, she became a teacher, had severe difficulty relating to men, had several abusive relationships, was overweight, overused drugs, and finally sought psychotherapy.

Impression: Sounds like a mother with a narcissistic personality disorder and a daughter with either a borderline personality disorder or a narcissistic personality disorder.

McDevitt reports on a third child:

The mother seemed to provide positive support that turned out to be a form of infantilizing: protecting her daughter from meeting challenges. The attachment was secure until the 19th month, when, after suffering an infection, the daughter regressed and clung to her mother. She overcame this in the rapprochement stage. As an adult, she was shy, inhibited, and had difficulty relating to men, and finally had successful psychotherapy for a psychoneurosis.

Impression: This child survived the preoedipal stage and became conflicted in the oedipal stage.

All three showed insecure attachment and one resolved it through the resolution of the rapprochement crisis. These three confirm the idea of insecure attachment, but we must await the follow-up of the rest for a more definite conclusion.

The following evidence raises the possibility that at least half of the infants Mahler studied showed insecure rather than secure attachment.

1. The description of the mothers' difficulties supporting individuation in the symbiotic stage in 11 of the 21 children.
2. The insecure attachment shown by these children.
3. The insecure attachment and later problems seen on follow-up of the three children.
4. Mahler's developing her hypothesis from work with psychotic children and having a strong motive to find it in "normal" children.
5. Stern's not finding an autistic or symbiotic stage or splitting or grandiosity.
6. Attachment researchers' not finding unawareness of the mother in practicing or ambivalence in rapprochement.

7. Mahler's theory regarding symbiosis—separation–individuation—fits the personality disorders like a glove.

This conclusion must remain tentative because of the fragile nature of the evidence. Further evidence should be forthcoming when the rest of the subjects are seen in follow-up. Perhaps many of them will show secure attachment.

How are we to understand this apparent contradiction between Mahler's theory and the findings of Stern and the attachment researchers, especially since Mahler's theory has been and continues to be such a rich stimulus to clinical exploration, and yet at the same time is being challenged as not reflecting normal development.

Two features may help to explain this paradox: First, Mahler's notion of symbiosis and separation–individuation was derived from the study of psychotic children, and her motivation for the normal study was to confirm her hypothesis that symbiosis and separation–individuation so clearly present in patients would also be a part of normal healthy development. This bias might have interfered with her being open-minded about the evidence, and may have influenced her unwittingly to interpret it to reflect that bias, despite her being a conscientious and dedicated researcher. It can happen to the best of us.

The fact that her theory and observations seemed to fit so snugly with the work on personality disorders in adults may actually mean that that is exactly what they were—a theory of the early developmental problems of children with secure attachment.

What is the clinician who has to deal with patients every day to make of this? Should we throw out the work that was originally partially based on Mahler's theory and look for a new framework and new therapeutic approach. The answer is No. The work remains as effective today as it ever was.

It's important to remember that Mahler was a pioneer with all the problems that breaking new ground brings with it, and her vital contribution was the pioneering of child-observation research and the emphasis on the importance of the mother's contribution to the development of the sense of self, identity, and ego structure of the child. She led the way and her emphasis on the surpassing importance of the mother to the emergence of the child's self has been validated by the other researchers despite their remaining disagreements. Beyond that,

Schore[1.36] has confirmed her theory of symbiosis on the neurobiological level.

Promises and Pitfalls of Developmental Research

A number of cautions are necessary in reflecting on the developmental research. First, Mahler and Stern attempted to deduce what was going on in the infant's psyche from observation of the behavior. It is important to keep in mind that these are hypotheses, educated guesses, as no one can know what actually transpires in an infant's psyche. Bowlby managed to avoid this pitfall by focusing on behavior, but later attachment researchers are now raising hypotheses about intrapsychic life.

Second, there is a long distance between the research infant and the clinical infant. The research infant provides maximum observation and minimum subjective report whereas the clinical infant provides maximum self-report with a minimum of clinical observation. It is a far reach from one to the other, which allows for the possibility of many differences.

The level of proof in clinical work is not based on the passage from normal to the pathological—the developmental researchers themselves have difficulty predicting what will happen in the future from looking at the present in normals, so the leap from normals to the pathological is too great to provide valid proof. The proof comes from the repetition of the pathology in the transference acting out and in the transference, and then in the early history as it confirms what was seen in the repetition. Of course, there are also pitfalls in this approach that have to be kept in mind.

These researchers used smaller numbers so that ultimately much larger numbers would be necessary to validate the findings.

Other variables also must be taken into consideration, such as temperament as reported on by Chess and Thomas,[1.40] and culture, which is a powerful determinant of development. For example, the mothers of the Gussi Tribe in Kenya are appalled at American mothers' not maintaining constant physical closeness to the young child.

Another problem has to do with definitions: Mahler speaks of average mothers with their normal children. These words—*normal, average, healthy*—are often defined differently by different people

Arrest of Normal Development or Pathological Development

The attachment researchers make the point that normal development is very different from the development of patients. They suggest that patients, rather than having an arrest of normal development, have a pathological form of development related to difficulties with attachment beginning in the first year of life. This view suggests the Achilles' heel of attempts to theorize retrospectively from patient reconstructions in order to form hypotheses about normal development. This would apply as well to Kernberg's theory about splitting and to the development of the internalized object relations of Melanie Klein and to Kohut's developmental theories. They are suggesting that these theories may have relevance for patients, but are not relevant to the development of normal infants.

This shift in point of view to a pathological development poses more questions than it answers. The attachment researchers are now doing in reverse what they criticized Mahler and Kernberg for doing. They are using material from normal development to hypothesize about pathological development, and it falls prey to the same scientific errors as does raising hypotheses about normals from the study of pathology.

For example, we certainly see in personality disorders areas of healthy or adaptive or normal development; if patients didn't have these, they would be psychotic. How is it possible to square this with the idea of pathological development from the beginning? As a matter of fact, as therapists, we rely on the healthy part of the patient's ego strength as a basis for many of our clinical decisions.

Developmental Theories and the Personality Disorders

Freud, in his clinical work, shifted his theoretical models to illuminate better the clinical problem he was studying; for example, from the topographic to the structural model. Similarly, we must look at these developmental theories as working models that may illuminate better one part or another of the clinical problems we are studying.

Mahler's theory, whether derived from secure or insecure attachment studies, still is very helpful to illuminate the clinical issues engendered by the borderline personality disorder, and to a lesser extent, by the narcissistic personality disorder. Stern's theory seems to illuminate best through his emphasis on attunement-to-the-self work with the narcissistic personality disorder. The attachment theorists, with their focus on how the child maintains attachment with the maternal object, seem to illuminate best their work with the schizoid and paranoid disorders and the psychopathic personality. Schore's work illuminates the neurological wiring underpinning the sense of self, reinforces Mahler's notion of the importance of the role of the mother in the development of the wiring necessary for the sense of self, and opens up the possibility that psychotherapy may be effective by changing the wiring.

Chapter Two

The Role of the Mother or Primary Caretaker in the Borderline Personality Disorder

25 Years Later

Some 25 years ago (1975), I published a paper (with D. Rinsley)[2.27] on the role of the mother in the genesis and intrapsychic structure of the borderline personality disorder. This paper was partially derived from Mahler's[2.23] theory of "normal" separation-individuation, as well as from many years of clinical research on both borderline adolescents[2.31,2.35] and borderline adults.[2.29–2.37] The findings were confirmed by a formal research follow-up study of adolescents treated with the model developed from these studies.[2.31]

Keeping in mind that memory is a reconstruction (not a photograph), can be altered intrapsychically after the event, and is dependent on the state of mind at the time of recall,[2.43] the conclusions of the paper derived not only from the adolescent and adult patients' reports, which could be distorted, but from clinical observation of the parents of adolescents in marital and group therapy and their interactions with the adolescent in family therapy. This additional evidence, for the most part, confirmed the patients' reports.

Beyond that, psychoanalytic psychotherapy with borderline adults inevitably led to the difficulty with the mother when the defenses against the abandonment depression were overcome and the self began to emerge. These reports reflected the developmental interactions with the mother more than did the aggressively derived object relations representations described by Kernberg.[2.15, 2.16] It's not that the latter do not play a role; it's a matter of emphasis—mine being more developmental and Kernberg's being more a constitutional excess of aggression.

Sources of the Theory

A theory of etiology developed that had three facets: nature, nuture, and fate. Nature consisted of the genetic input expressed in the capacity of the drive for individuation. Fate referred to the occurrence of environmental separation stresses between ages 2 and 3. Nurture—as the title of the paper implied—referred to the mother's difficulty in providing emotional supplies and support for the child's individuating self to emerge. This applied to a wide range of maternal behaviors: mothers who physically or sexually abuse a child, the borderline mother who clings to the child's regressive behavior to defend against her own abandonment depression and is not able to support the child's individuation, a narcissistic mother who requires the child to idealize her; a schizoid mother who cannot tolerate closeness to the child and withdraws, a psychopathic mother who either neglects the child or uses the child as a tool for her satisfaction, a mother who cannot tolerate the child's dependence and pushes the child to be independent prematurely.

Regardless of this wide range of maternal behaviors, the key psychodynamic impact and the final common pathway for the child is to experience this as a loss of part of himself or herself that leads to an abandonment depression and a developmental arrest of the ego and the object relations. The interactions with the mother are deeply internalized to produce the object relations unit of intrapsychic structure and the central psychodynamic theme: self-activation leads to separation anxiety and abandonment depression, which leads to defense. For example, with the borderline mother, the twin themes of availability for regression, but unavailability for individuation, dominate the intrapsychic structure and motivate the psychodynamic theme. Psychoanalytic psychotherapy[2.28] developed on this basis was demonstrated to be effective by systematic follow-up research.[2.31]

The theory linked a specific interpersonal interaction between mother and child to its internalization in the form of the intrapsychic structure and the central psychodynamic theme, and finally to a therapeutic approach to deal with that structure.

Is the mother the sole contributor to the etiology? No. There is a relative interplay between the strength of the child's genetic drive for individuation and the amount of maternal libidinal availability necessary to facilitate that individuation. Some children may need very little support whereas others may have a genetic vulnerability and require a lot, and still others, because of genetic deficiencies, may not be able to utilize ideal support. Beyond that, sometimes the environmental separation stress, such as the mother's being ill or taken away during the critical separation–individuation stage, may by itself precipitate a borderline personality disorder.

In these times when 60% of married women work, the question of the degree of maternal availability necessary is a crucial one. Am I saying that working mothers produce borderline disorders? Absolutely not. The issue is not absolute availability, but providing "good enough" availability to afford a psychological function for the child. The working mother is present in the morning and evening and her attitude toward the child is also conveyed by the substitute caretakers she selects. The amount of availability she will have to provide depends on, among other things, the strength of the child's drive for individuation.

Some resist the idea of the importance of maternal availability, calling it "mother bashing," as occurred with the schizophrenogenic mother. I think, however, that they may be under the sway of the almost universal tendency to hold on to the positive image of "mother." This need causes its adherents to deny some important facts about development revealed in the study of normal development, as well as in its failures, as seen in the borderline personality disorder:

The female child is born with the instinctual capacity to mother, but not the developmental capacity. This is a hard-won developmental achievement, with many possibilities of going astray along the way. Perhaps it is more accurate to wonder that so many do it so well rather than to be surprised that so many others have so much trouble. Ainsworth[2.4] reported that 62% of American families had children with secure attachment.

Neurobiological Research and the Mother Role in the Development of the Neurological Structure Essential to Developing a Sense of Self[2.44]

Recent neurobiological research[2.44] has made clear that the mother's role is, if anything, even more vital neurologically than it was found to be psychologically. The brain at birth is extremely immature, and in the first year of postnatal life, it increases in size 2½ times, with most of this increase in the cortex. At birth, a child is practically without a cortex. The cortex provides an inhibiting function so that the mother must provide this function until the child's own cortex develops: "The mother is the major source of the environmental stimulation that facilitates (or inhibits) the experience-dependent maturation of the child's developing neurological structure. Her essential role as the psychological regulator of the child's immature psychophysiological systems directly influences the child's biochemical growth processes, which support the genesis of new structures."[2.44]

The neurological development of the brain is not continuous, but occurs in spurts and in critical phases when environmental input is vital for the successful completion of the phase of development.

Schore[2.44] theorizes that a critical phase for the emergence of self-regulation of affect occurs at 10 to 12 months of age, and a second one at 14 to 16 months of age. It is crucial that the mother's interaction be appropriate and supportive, helping the child to regulate his or her affect for the appropriate wiring to occur. Genetics are responsible for the existence of the neuronal structures, but interaction with the maternal environment is crucial to the growth and the wiring that is established between them so that the mother plays a significant role, and we no longer speak of nature or nurture but of nature and nurture. One does not occur without the other. The mother's role is as vital neurologically as it is psychologically.

Denial of the Mother's Role in Clinical Theories

The borderline patient's wide variation in level of functioning; the patient's capacity to evoke through projective identification the therapist's countertransference, particularly to the patient's neediness; as well as the patient's tendency to respond chameleon-like to whatever environment he or she may occupy; have resulted in a veritable Tower of Babel of voices proclaiming different points of view on how to treat the borderline patient.

This confusion is further reinforced by the replacement of the mother's role by vague notions of a biological vulnerability or generalizations, such as disruptions of good-enough mothering or failures of a sustaining internal object that are not followed through to the intrapsychic structure and its treatment requirements.

This denial of the mother's role and how it is internalized deprives the psychotherapist of the key pathway necessary to design a specific and effective psychotherapy. The only approach left is to design measures to deal only with the contemporary psychopathology, overlooking its source and its key integrating psychodynamic. This denial leads to many different points of view, examples of which are described below.

Biological Vulnerability

1. Paris, Joel, M.D.[2.41]—*Borderline Personality Disorder: What Is It? What Causes It? How Can We Treat It?*

   "No single factor explains its development. Rather, multiple risk factors, which can be biological, psychological, or social, play a role in its etiology."
2. Trestment, Robert L., M.D.[2.47]—*The Challenge of Borderline Personality Disorder*

   "Etiology: An evolving framework shared by many researchers in the field today suggests that for severe mental illness, such as BPD, there first must be an inherited biological vulnerability. This vulnerability may then either set the stage for a so-called 'second hit' (an environmental influence that triggers the expression of the disorder), or a time-linked expression that develops regardless of the environment."
3. Oldham, John M., M.D.[2.40]—*Borderline Personality Disorder: The Treatment Dilemma*

   "Although strong evidence is still lacking, there is general agreement that there is probably a genetic susceptibility to develop BPD, at least in many cases: (1) a particular temperament, (2) an environment that amplifies the psychological vulnerability associated with the temperament."

4. Siever, Larry J., M.D.[2.45]—*The Biology of Borderline Personality Disorder*

   "The two hallmark psychobiologic vulnerabilities or temperamental predispositions are affective instability and impulsive aggression."

5. Linehan, Marsha M., Ph.D.[2.21]—*Dialectical Behavior Therapy (DBT) for Borderline Personality Disorder*

   "The fundamental biological disorder is in the *emotion regulation system* and may be due to genetics, intrauterine factors before birth, traumatic events in early development that permanently affect the brain, or some combination of these factors. The environmental disorder is any set of circumstances that pervasively punish, traumatize, or neglect this emotional vulnerability specifically, or the individual's emotional self generally, termed the invalidating environment."

6. Vela, Ricardo M., M.D.[2.48]—*Borderline Personality Disorder: Is It Possible in Children Under Twelve?*

   "There seems to be a variety of constitutional and external factors associated with the development of this condition. There are some children who appear to be born this way. It is as though their internal 'emotional thermostat,' which regulates emotions, is broken from birth and, even with adequate child rearing, they cannot escape becoming borderline children. Some children have signs of brain damage and positive findings discovered in neurological examinations. These findings probably indicate some 'defect' in the nervous system that predisposes or makes them more vulnerable to developing this disorder, especially if they are raised under adverse social conditions. Other children who develop borderline personality have been victims of physical or sexual abuse. In this case, their emotional thermostat is broken as a result of trauma and they lose the capacity of regulating their fluctuating emotions and the capacity to soothe themselves. Once it

> starts, their anxiety cannot be contained or 'brought down' and it escalates into panic. Impulsive outbursts simply cannot be regulated by such an individual, resulting in explosive, out-of-control behavior."

The above denials persist despite the avalanche of data from all the psychoanalytic child-observation studies of normal infant development. Whatever their differences, all of these researchers (Mahler,[2.23] Stern,[2.46] Bowlby,[2.5] Ainsworth,[2.4] Emde,[2.8] Brazelton,[2.7] are unanimous in their view that the mother's libidinal availability and support of the infant's emerging self are vital to the development of the secure attachment, the sense of self, and identity. And now this view is further supported by neurological research.[2.44]

Minimizing the Role of the Mother

The following theorists' difficulty with integrating the role of the mother into their theories leads to an approach that is one step removed from the key problem.

Kernberg's Object Relations[2.14–2.16]

Kernberg has contributed much to our understanding of the borderline patient. However, he sees the etiology more from a Kleinian perspective as combining a genetic input with a constitutional excess of aggression, with the interaction with the mother playing a minor part, and, therefore, he sees the intrapsychic structure mainly determined by the internal excess aggression. Kernberg is able to minimize the issue of the developmental interaction with the mother by concentrating mostly on its intrapsychic representations infiltrated with excess aggression. More recently, Kernberg* noted, "The most important cause of severe personality disorders is severe chronic traumatic experiences, such as physical or sexual abuse, severe deprivation of love, severe neglect, unavailable parental objects as familial dispositions that can lead to the

*Interview with Otto F. Kernberg, M.D., developer of an object relations psychoanalytic therapy for borderline personality disorder. *American Journal of Psychotherapy, 52*(2) Spring, 1988.

development of personality disorders." He seems here to be shifting from the excess aggression view to a developmental view. He does not take it a step farther to the position that the key psychodynamic impact of these "traumas" is the lack of support of the object for the developing self. I see the issue more as combining the genetic input with maternal libidinal unavailability for the emerging self, and, therefore, the intrapsychic structure represents more interaction than the excess of aggression, although it is both.

There are many similarities between my approach and Kernberg's. We both recommend expressive or psychoanayltic psychotherapy where possible rather than supportive therapy, and we use such concepts as maintenance of therapeutic neutrality, the notion of the intrapsychic structure, the ego defects, and splitting.

He emphasizes working through the aggression whereas I emphasize the working through of the abandonment depression, which has an aggressive component. I use the concept of a disorder of the self, with the key psychodynamic being the disorder of the self triad: self-activation leads to separation anxiety and abandonment depression, which leads to defense. The psychoanalytic psychotherapy revolves around this theme and the therapist's task is to identify its clinical vicissitudes and confront defense. This gives great precision to the work.

Kernberg does not use this concept, which, in my view, keeps his interventions at a certain distance from the key issue of the self and its triad. Kernberg sees the patient in the initial part of treatment as relating by primitive transferences that require "clarification" whereas I see it as transference acting out, which requires confrontation.

Kernberg stresses the interpretation of the alternating self and object representations in the transference. However, he does not link these to the borderline triad, which is the key motivation for their alternating presentation. He sees interpretation of these split units as promoting integration, which I do not. I think integration of the split self and object representations comes about through growth as a consequence of working through the abandonment depression.

He also emphasizes the interpretation of transference, whereas in my view there is no transference until later in the treatment. He views transference acting out as a transitional dynamically caused transference defensive operation. I see it more as the principal defensive aspect of the borderline personality organization, which must be dealt with first in psychotherapy. Also, he stresses interpretation in the early phase, whereas I reserve interpretation until a therapeutic alliance and transference have been established by confrontation of the transference acting out.

Kohut and Self Psychology[2.19, 2.20]

Role of the Mother—Defective Mirroring

Kohut's conception of why and how the mother's mirroring function is defective seems to me to describe only part of the picture. He describes the mother as lacking empathy for the child's grandiose exhibitionistic self. In other words, she is not able to understand or respond for a variety of possible reasons, none of which seem to have anything specifically to do with that child. The reasons may be her narcissism, her depression, her psychotic state, and so on. Although this no doubt is true in some cases, far more often in my experience, the mother's defective mirroring springs from a specific emotional withdrawal, because this specific child is expressing his or her own unique self.

This self-expression interrupts the child's resonating with the mother's projections and thereby upsets her intrapsychic equilibrium. More important, it seems to me, Kohut overlooks the profound effects of the other part of this theme, the mother's reward for those regressive behaviors that fulfill her projections, thereby gratifying her clinging and relieving her anxiety. This theme is overlooked, despite the fact that it is described a number of times[2.20]:

> On innumerable occasions she appeared to have been totally absorbed in the child—overcaressing him, completely in tune with every nuance of his needs and wishes—only to withdraw from him suddenly, either by turning her attention totally to other interests or by grossly and grotesquely misunderstanding his needs and wishes.

This denial reached its height in his argument against a disorder of the self resulting from instinctual fixation on oral fixation points, with corresponding developmental arrest of the ego as the result of "addiction to infantile gratification." It is not addiction to infantile gratification as such, but the push–pull of reward for regression and withdrawal for separation–individuation. In other words, the emotional state of being cared for, being fed, induced by the infantile gratification, stands in dramatic contrast to the stark affective experience of abandonment depression.

In his argument against such a possibility, Kohut states that it could only be brought about by parents who indulged pregenital drives and blocked the child's phallic genital needs: "I don't believe such a decisive blocking could be carried out even by parents who are in minimal empathic contact with the maturational aspirations of their child.[2.63, p. 73] In this statement, the author denies that the mother's responses do indeed block not only phallic-genital needs, but also, and more important, the primitive and fundamental need for individuation—to be a separate, autonomously functioning individual.

Clinical

Kohut was the first to emphasize the clinical manifestations of the grandiose self and omnipotent object representations in the narcissistic personality disorder and the difficulties with real self-activation. He followed Fairbairn[2.9] in seeing the disorders of the self as being at a preoedipal rather than oedipal level and that excess aggression was developmental, not constitutional.

However, he lumped all the personality disorders into one category, disorders of the self, and all received the same treatment. The issue is further confused by his using the term "borderline," but referring only to the borderline psychotic; in other words, patients who could not be analyzed because they would become psychotic. When the self psychology therapist uses the interpretation of empathic failure with a borderline patient before a therapeutic alliance has been established, the therapist reinforces the rewarding unit defense and brings treatment to a halt.

Theory

There are many problems from a theoretical point of view. First is the theory of the independent line of narcissism: The self as a bipolar self object does not separate from the object, but matures from infantile archaic forms to mature through the self-object functions of the parents (mirroring and idealizing). The reality of the object representation doesn't matter, only its self-object functions. The parents' personalities don't matter, only their self-object function. In other words, "the self object is experienced as the self's object." The sense of its possession and entitlement is unconscious. The therapist focuses on the inner experiences to the exclusion of reality.

There are other problems. Kohut equates the father's idealizing function between 4 and 6 with the mother's mirroring between 0 and 3. If the mother's mirroring has not laid down a firm sense of self, in my view, the father is unable to compensate for it in an effective way. There are semantic confusions. What we call defense, he calls the patient's efforts to repair. He uses splitting, which is conventionally thought of as between self and object representations, as vertical between affect and defense and horizontal between past and present.

Psychotherapy

The aim of treatment is to establish an empathic bond or self-object transference that repairs the patient's defects through transmuting internalizations. This suggests a kind of fantasy reparenting—needs not met as a child are met in fantasy in treatment. The reality dimension is missing.

Kohut objects to a concept of therapeutic alliance based on reality and calls self-object transference a therapeutic alliance. Since it ignores reality, this is a contradiction in terms. By joining the patient's narcissistic fusion fantasies through the self-object transference, the therapist attempts to establish a therapeutic alliance that can only be established by helping the person's self to emerge from those defensive fantasies into reality. The central confusion about boundaries and reality limits is seen in his view of what promotes change and growth: When the therapist deemphasizes the real object and the real therapeutic alliance and enters the patient's self-object transference, he or she joins the patient's defenses, rather than helps the patient overcome them.

Adler[2.2, 2.3]

In 1979, Adler and Buie, in a paper[2.2] on the borderline, offered the theory that the borderline's major vulnerability was the tenuous achievement of the capacity for affective object permanence or evocative memory and its regressive loss to recognition memory or earlier under specific stresses, which resulted in the patient's feeling the loss of an internal soothing object and, therefore, experiencing an intolerance of being alone.

Their notion of the causes of this vulnerability are variously stated as follows: possible empathic parental failures during the substages of separation-individuation; failures of a sustaining object or of the holding environment; relative inadequacy or disruptions of good-enough mothering; chronic failures of good-enough mothering in the second year of life. In addition, quoting Freud, brief traumatic separations can produce severe vulnerability.

Since the patient has lost the intrapsychic sense of a soothing object representation and, therefore, cannot tolerate being alone, they recommend that the therapist alter therapeutic neutrality to provide this external soothing object for the patient; for example, frequent brief telephone calls, extra appointments, or the provision of "transitional objects," such as the therapist's phone number on a piece of paper, a gift (perhaps a book), or the monthly bill (which the patient may carry in his or her wallet for weeks at a time).

Adler deals with the role of the mother in the etiology in a more general sense, that is, failures of the sustaining object, and does not go on to link it specifically with the mother's difficulty in supporting the child's emerging self. He quotes Piaget that object permanence occurs at about 18 months, and it has since been discovered by Stern that it takes place at approximately 3 months of age. The authors do mention that this difficulty with the evocative memory tends to arise more often in sicker patients who are more at the psychotic level. In my experience, this occurs primarily in those patients. In that type of patient, it may be therapeutic to provide parameters that promote the development of the soothing object. However, in the patients who do have the capacity for evocative memory, the provision of these parameters requires a stepping into the rewarding unit, reinforcing resistance, and bringing the possibility of intrapsychic change to a halt.

Gunderson[2.13]

In 1996, Gunderson took Adler and Buie's work on the intolerance of being alone as his principal theme. Gunderson refers to etiology as follows: The early relationship of caretakers is sufficiently inconsistent and unstable that "a soothing introject failed to occur." He then refers to Bowlby's attachment theory, quoting Ainsworth to suggest that the insecure-attachment patterns defined by Ainsworth as anxious/ambivalent and disoriented/disorganized are the kinds of patterns seen in borderline histories and develop in response to primary caregivers who are depressed, disturbed, or abusive, all of which are seen in borderline histories. Gunderson, like Adler before him, refers to the difficulties in the mother–child relationship, but again in more general terms, and does not relate it specifically to the emergence of the child's self because he does not use the concept of the self. Gunderson then does Adler one better by emphasizing that the intolerance of being alone is the central feature of all "borderline patients," which indicates the therapeutic use of various parameters in order to promote the internalization of a soothing object.

My research[2.24–2.37] and many years of clinical experience, as well as the work of many others,[2.11, 2.4–2.16, 2.19, 2.20, 2.38, 2.39] do not support this self-psychology hypothesis. The only borderline patients who could not evoke the soothing image of the therapist when he or she was not there were some, not all, lower-level primitive patients whose early developmental arrest and weak ego made it impossible.

Adler and Buie[2.2, 2.3] emphasized this as follows: "Patients closer to psychosis experience this more frequently and intensely."

In other words, the difficulty had more to do with the patient's level of developmental arrest than with the fact that the patient had a borderline disorder.

Condensing Different Clinical Types

By combining lower-level patients, some of whom may have a defect in the capacity to evoke the image of a soothing object when the real object is not there, with mid and upper-level patients who do not have this defect, Gunderson puts two very different clinical types in the same category, which leads to confusion about the treatment. According to Gunderson, both types require the same approach: increased availability of the therapist.

My own view stresses that these two different types require two different approaches. The therapeutic issue here is the patient's capacity to tolerate the therapist's neutrality, which is a condition for being able to do psychoanalytic psychotherapy. Some lower-level patients cannot tolerate therapeutic neutrality because their ego structures cannot contain their painful affects, and, therefore, they are not candidates for psychoanalytic psychotherapy. They respond better to a more active, supportive therapy, which, while helpful, is limited in that it does not offer enduring intrapsychic change.

Middle- and high-level patients, on the other hand, are candidates for psychoanalytic psychotherapy because they can evoke the image of the soothing object when the real object is not present and, therefore, can tolerate therapeutic neutrality. Beyond that, psychoanalytic psychotherapy offers far more potential for enduring intrapsychic change than does the more active supportive therapy. When borderline patients who do not have a defect are treated as if they do by increased availability, and so on, the therapist resonates with the patient's projections, reinforces defense, and does not create the conditions required to promote internalization and change.

What are these conditions? Internalization and change occur when the therapist maintains a neutral stance, which becomes the reality screen against which the patient's clinging and distancing transference acting out are confronted and the resultant transference projections are identified, measured, and worked through. In this process, the patient's projections on the therapist subside, a therapeutic alliance is formed, and the resolution of the tension between the projections and the therapeutic alliance opens the way to internalization, change, and growth.

"Neediness" and Therapeutic Needs

The borderline patient has a well-earned reputation for being "needy" and demanding, and for being able to evoke countertransference in the therapist to that behavior. These two characteristics, acting in concert, make it difficult for the therapist to carry out a crucial initial therapeutic task: to determine the relationship of the patient's "neediness" to the patient's therapeutic needs.

The issue is further complicated by the patient's initial testing behavior, which has earned the initial phase of therapy the name "testing phase." The patient has been able to maintain some emotional equilibrium by his or her defenses, while denying that they are destructive. If he or she enters into a therapeutic alliance, the patient will give up his or her reliance on the defenses and rely on the therapist and therapy. Since the patient doesn't know the therapist, he or she must test the therapist in order to answer two questions: Is he or she competent, and is he or she trustworthy? When these are answered by the therapist's interventions, the middle- or upper-level patient is able to give up destructive defenses and use therapy to deal with emotions.

The crucial issue, then, in the testing phase, is to decide whether the patient's ostensible neediness is a true therapeutic need (as in a lower-level patient) or a testing behavior (as in a middle- or higher-level patient). Confrontation of the behavior usually answers the test and helps to make the decision as to whether this is a lower-level patient who needs supportive therapy or a higher-level patient who is a candidate for psychoanalytic psychotherapy.

Classical Psychoanalysts[2.6, 2.1–2.12]

Classical psychoanalysts recommend classical psychoanalysis (Abend, Pordter, Willick, Giovacchini, and Boyer and Gabbard). They insist on interpretation of the transference where there is no transference until later in the treatment and where the interpretation of transference always plays a subordinate role to the management of defenses. Classical analysis is designed to deal with oedipal conflict and is not effective with preoedipal conflict. Many high-level borderline patients are diagnosed as psychoneurotic and receive this approach, which does not get to the core of their problem.

The Kleinian Classical Analysts[2.17, 2.18]

These analysts emphasize the importance of a constitutional excess of aggression, minimizing the role of the mother. They also recommend psychoanalysis using the Kleinian approach, which, in my view, is too heavily involved in making deep interpretations too early in the treatment before a therapeutic alliance and transference are achieved.

Linehan and Dialectical Behavior Therapy[2.21]

Linehan ignores the role of the mother and psychodynamics entirely.

Dialectical behavior therapy (DBT) sees the borderline patient's central problems as consisting of emotional vulnerability and the defects in skills needed to regulate emotion. The treatment program has four parts:

1. Enhancement of capabilities: A psychoeducational skills training session of 2½ hours once a week.
2. Enhancement of motivation: Weekly one- and a half-hour sessions using cognitive and behavioral therapies to enhance motivation.
3. Enhancing generalization: This is to deal with environmental interactions that are obstacles to the treatment. It consists of phone consultations, family sessions.
4. Finally, weekly team consultations with all DBT therapists.

This approach was researched with suicidal and parasuicidal patients who were not responsive to other forms of therapy, and indeed it may be effective for these patients who, in all probability, do not have enough ego strength to benefit from any form of psychoanalytic psychotherapy. However, under the pressure of managed care, DBT is now being advocated for the treatment of all borderline patients. The problem with using this approach with patients who have the capacity for psychoanalytic psychotherapy is that it ignores the need for therapeutic neutrality to protect the fragility of the patient's self. Instead it provides massive input in terms of cognitive behavior therapies and education, which relieves the patient of responsibility for activating himself or herself and stimulates the rewarding unit defense—and treatment comes to a halt. It is possible to get transient behavioral change on this basis, but it is not possible to get intrapsychic change.

Psychopharmacologists[2.45, 2.49]

Psychopharmacologists ignore the role of the mother and the intrapsychic structure and developmental conflicts and give medication for what they call "dimensions" of pathology, such as affective instability and impulse control. The patient's intrapsychic structure is ignored and, therefore, cannot change. This may be appropriate for lower-level patients who have great difficulty in functioning and are not available for psychoanalytic psychotherapy, but not for patients who have the capacity for psychoanalytic psychotherapy. However, the use of medication in addition to psychotherapy rather than instead of it is often important.

Goldstein[2.12]

Goldstein follows Kernberg in recommending dealing with the transference when there is no transference. He offers a graduated approach depending on the degree of psychopathology, but he again does not include a concept of the mother, so the treatment does not get to the core. He also supports the idea that one can do supportive and analytic therapy at the same time whereas I see them as competing with each other. One cannot resonate with a resistance and also analyze it.

Meissner[2.38, 2.39]

Meissner refers to the literature on the role of the mother but does not integrate it into his approach. Our points of view agree, particularly with regard to the importance of therapeutic neutrality, maintaining the frame and therapeutic alliance and the use of confrontation. I disagree with his view about the nature and importance of transference acting out. Again, I see it as the primary continuing defense that is constant and developmental in origin, and must be dealt with by confrontation to help the patient convert it into therapeutic alliance and transference. Meissner, like Kernberg, sees it as a transitional dynamic caused by the transference interaction. Meissner also emphasizes transference interpretation, and I see it as useful only after the therapeutic alliance and transference have been established. Meissner notes how resistant borderline patients are to interpretation. In my view, this may be due to premature interpretations. Finally, in my view, he confuses the narcissistic disorder and Kohut's self psychology with the narcissistic or self pathology of the borderline. He also seems to feel that one can do supportive and analytic psychotherapy at the same time. I see them as competing with each other.

Changes in Development Object Relations Theory 25 Years Later

Mahler's[2.23] notion of the separation of the child's self-image from the symbiotic relationship with the mother has not been replicated by other developmental researchers studying the development of normal children. For example, Stern[2.46] found that the child is prewired to perceive the mother as separate from birth. Beyond that, he found that there is no autistic or symbiotic stage, and attachment researchers found that there was no relative unawareness of the mother in the practicing stage or any ambivalence in the rapprochement stage. Neither Stern nor the attachment researchers found grandiosity or splitting. These findings raise the possibility that Mahler's[2.23] study may not have been of normals, but of insecure attachment—the type often seen in the personality disorders. This would help to explain why it fits so well and was such a crucial contributor to the wealth of study and progress in the treatment of personality disorders. In other words, her model fits the personality disorders more than it fits the normal. The attachment researchers have suggested that we should not call it the arrest of normal development but rather pathological development.[2.22]

Mahler,[2.23] Kernberg,[2.15, 2.16] Kohut,[2.19, 2.20] and Melanie Klein[2.17] ? have all advanced retrospective theories about normal development from studying pathology, and it would appear that these retrospective theories do not hold for normal development, especially when it is studied by researchers without bias. However, we still find their theories of help in our work with borderline personality disorders because symbiosis and separation are prime issues with these patients, as are aggression, idealization, and projection.

My theory, that the mother's unavailability has a great deal to do with the failure of the self to develop in the borderline personality disorder, has been vastly reinforced by brain neurological research, which suggests that nature sets the genes, that is, the neurons, but their connection or wiring is "experience dependent" on the mother's support during critical stages of the development of self-regulation in the brain. The mother's availability is as important neurologically as psychologically.

In the ensuing years, I've added to the concept of the borderline personality disorder[2.34, 2.36] that there is a pathological arrest of the self, as well as of the ego and of the object relations, and that this arrested self is a key feature of the disorder that is expressed in the key psychodynamic theme: separation-individuation leads to separation anxiety and abandonment depression, which leads to defense. The diagnostic category becomes borderline personality disorder of the self and the key therapeutic intervention is confrontation of the maladaptive aspect of the defense.

This developmental self and object relations approach places primary emphasis on the contribution of the preoedipal mother–child tie to the development of the borderline personality disorder, and the therapeutic model is derived from that conception. The effectiveness of this model has been tested by follow-up research.[2,30] The continued denial and minimization of the role of the mother lead to confusion about both the psychopathology and the treatment.

Diagnosis

Diagnosis by DSM-IV

The advantage of the DSM-IV approach is that, based on symptoms—the most obvious and easiest replicated phenomena—and not on any theory, it can be used to test all theories. The handicaps of DSM-IV from the perspective of the borderline patient is that since it is based on symptoms, it's based on the most transient and evanescent of borderline phenomena. Also, the symptom categories are heavily weighted toward the lower-level borderline patient with difficulty functioning, so that many upper-level borderline patients would not receive this diagnosis.

DSM-IV Symptoms

1. Frantic efforts to avoid real or imagined abandonment. Note: Do not include suicidal or self-mutilating behavior, which is covered in criterion 5.
2. A pattern of unstable and intense interpersonal relationships characterized by alternating between extremes of idealization and devaluation.
3. Identity disturbance: markedly and persistently unstable self-image or sense of self.
4. Impulsivity in at least two areas that are potentially self-damaging (e.g., spending, sex, substance abuse, reckless driving, binge eating). Note: Do not include suicidal or self-mutilating behavior, which is covered in criterion 5.
5. Recurrent suicidal behavior, gestures, or threats, or self-mutilating behavior.
6. Affective instability due to a marked reactivity of mood (e.g., intense episodic dysphoria, irritability, or anxiety

usually lasting a few hours and only rarely more than a few days).

7. Chronic feelings of emptiness.
8. Inappropriate, intense anger or difficulty controlling anger (e.g., frequent displays of temper, constant anger, recurrent physical fights).
9. Transient, stress-related paranoid ideation or severe dissociative symptoms.

Diagnosis from a Developmental Self and Object Relations Approach

Maternal Libidinal Unavailability and the Split Object Relations Unit

The mother of the borderline patient finds herself[2.26, 2.27, 2.35] unable to support the patient's emerging self during the rapprochement stage of individuation (Maher[2.23]) or the intersubjective stage (Stern[2.46]). Some mothers can be available in the earlier stages if a child clings, but are threatened by the child's individuation. Others cannot tolerate the early attachment and push the patient to separate prematurely. These mothers suffer from self-pathology, are borderline, narcissistic, psychotic, and so on, or, as Bowlby indicated, may be physically absent.

The key issue is that there is something in the mother's personality that makes it difficult to impossible for her to provide emotional supplies and support or attunement to the child's emerging self. I don't mean here the conventional notion of nurture and feeding and caretaking and protection, but the mother's capacity to identify the unique individuated aspects of the emerging self and provide emotional supplies and support for that development. There has been some confusion that this notion applies only to the mother who clings. It also applies to the mother who distances or the mother who prematurely pushes the child toward independence. None of these acknowledge the child's emerging self.

The mother depersonifies the child, cannot relate to the child as he or she is, tends to project upon the child the image of someone from her own past, and treats him or her as if he or she were that person. The needs of the child's real self for acknowledgment go unacknowledged. The mother is unable to respond to his or her unfolding individuality, and he or she early learns to disregard his or her own potentials in order to preserve the source of emotional supply from the mother. Therefore, between the ages of 18 and 36 months, conflict develops in the child between his or her own developmental push for individuation and autonomy and the fear of the withdrawal of the mother's emotional supply that his growth would entail. The child needs her approval to develop ego structure and grow. If he or she grows, the supplies are withdrawn. This interaction is deeply internalized to form the split object relations unit and the split ego.

The Split Object Relations Unit

The object relations unit is split into two separate part units, each of which contains a part-self representation and a part-object representation and the affect that links the two representations. These two are derived from the internalization of two themes of interaction with the mother, and their content will vary, depending on the mother's responses to self-activation. A classical borderline mother responds to the child's regressive behavior by maintaining her libidinal availability and the efforts toward separation-individuation by withdrawing it. Thus are produced the two part units termed the withdrawing object relations part unit (WORU) and the rewarding object relations part unit (RORU), each of which has its own component, part-self representation, part-object representation, and linking affect. The withdrawing part unit is cathected or invested predominately with aggressive energy, the rewarding part with libidinal energy, and both remain separated from each other through the mechanism of the splitting defense.

Developmental Arrest of the Ego and the Self

In addition to the developmental arrested object relations unit, the ego structure itself and the self are developmentally arrested. The ego has a principal mechanism of defense of splitting, the function of which is to keep contradictory affective states separated from each other. Both remain conscious but they do not influence each other. Splitting also keeps apart the internalized self and object representations mutually linked with these affective states.

In addition to the splitting defense, there is a split ego. The ego is itself split into two parts, one of which functions according to the pleasure principle, and the other according to the reality principle. Beyond that, the development arrest of the ego leads to defects in ego functioning: poor reality perception, impulse control, frustration tolerance, and ego boundaries, and primitive mechanisms of defense, acting out, clinging, projection, projective identification, denial, and so on.

Impairments in the Sense of Self

One of the principal developments since my early publications on the borderline has been a shift in my perspective from seeing the disorder as a developmental arrest of the ego and object relations to seeing it as a developmental arrest of the sense of self with associated arrest of the ego and object relations.

This concept of the self differs from that of the holistic and self-psychology schools and is more in keeping with the object relations theory and ego psychology.

The term "real self" is used to refer to the total intrapsychic self representations of the patient and its associated object representation. The functions of this real self are to provide a vehicle for self-activation and for the maintenance of self-esteem through the mastery of reality. The term "real" is used to connote healthy or normal to emphasize that the representations of the real self have an important conscious reality component, even though unconscious and fantasy elements also contribute. This helps to differentiate the real self from the false selves of the patients with the disorder of the self, which are based on a defensive fantasy, not on reality, and are directed toward defense, not toward self-activation.

Some or all of the capacities of the real self are impaired in the borderline patient. These capacities are: spontaneity and aliveness of affect; the sense of self-entitlement; the capacity for self-activation, for acknowledgment of self-activation and maintenance of self-esteem, and for the soothing of painful affects, continuity of self, commitment, creativity, intimacy, and automomy. However, since I now view all of the personality disorders as disorders of the self, the self is impaired with all of them, and this impairment does not differentiate the borderline from the others. To do this, we must turn to the intrapsychic structure and the split object relations unit.

The Disorder of the Self

How does this defensive system operate? I've called it the borderline triad (later changed to disorder-of-the-self triad) when it became clear the triad occurred in all disorders of the self. The patient's efforts at self-activation lead to separation anxiety and abandonment depression, which leads to defense. In other words, efforts at self-activation, including participation in therapy, precipitate the withdrawing unit with its abandonment depression. To defend against this unit, the patient has two options. A pathological ego through the alliance with the rewarding unit can activate that unit. The patient gives up self-activation under the sway of the rewarding unit and is able to deny that he or she is behaving regressively and maladaptively. If the alliance is with the withdrawing unit, the patient activates the withdrawing unit and massively projects and acts it out, either with a distancing form of transference acting out or as external acting out. Seemingly, the patient has a Hobson's choice, either to feel bad and abandoned, or to defend against that feeling at the cost of adaptation to reality.

Diagnosis from the Developmental Self and Object Relations Approach

1. These are the same symptoms seen in DSM-IV, which, in my view, are the patient's calling card.
2. Separation-individuation precipating stress. The therapist must look for what I call separation-individuation stresses. Often they are as obvious as the loss of a parent or the separation or divorce of a husband and wife. Sometimes, however, they are subtle, as with the going away to school of an older sister who has been a mother substitute. The patient is generally unaware so the therapist must make it his or her job to ferret out precipitating stress. Individuation stresses occur when patients are placed in situations that require more capacity for indi-

viduation than they are able to muster, such as being promoted to head a corporation, a position in which they will have no one else on whom to rely.

3. The intrapsychic structure as outlined in the history of relationships with others, as well as in relationship with the therapist.
4. The developmental arrested ego seen in the primitive defense mechanisms and defects in ego functioning.
5. The disorder-of-the-self triad confirmed by confrontation.

Conclusion

Twenty-five years ago, I reported that the mother's difficulty in supporting the child's emerging self in the rapprochement stage was one of the key etiological agents in the borderline personality disorder. The child internalized this interpersonal interaction to form the intrapsychic structure. This led to a specific model of psychoanalytic psychotherapy to deal with that structure that was researched and found to be effective.

There is a trend in the field to deny or minimize the role of the mother despite the overwhelming evidence from all studies of normal development, as well as the confirming reports from the treatment of borderline patients. Those who deny speak of "genetic vulnerability plus environmental trauma." Those who minimize—mostly psychoanalysts—speak of excess aggression, or inconsistent caretaking, or failures of the soothing object. However, none of these make the difficulty the cornerstone of their therapeutic approach, thereby inevitably limiting the effectiveness of the treatment.

Part II

Clinical

Chapter Three

Diagnosis

A Psychodynamic Approach to the Borderline, Narcissistic, and Schizoid Personality Disorders

The shift in perspective from personality disorders to disorders of the self occurred as a result of the clinical observation that the central psychodynamic theme of all the personality disorders was what I call the disorders-of-the-self triad: self-activation leads to separation anxiety and abandonment depression, which leads to defense. Thus, in all the personality disorders, the key feature was the developmental arrest of the self, along with the developmental arrest of the ego and the object relations. This central focus on the self enabled the therapist to concentrate the key interventions on the defenses of the disorders-of-the-self triad.

The advantages of adding the self to the developmental, object relations approach are, in my view, as follows: It provides an architecture of the patient's inner emotions, affective state, and the self- and object-representations linked with that affective state, while also defining the defense mechanisms and ego functions associated with that state. It tells you what emotion is on center stage and how to intervene in the defense against that emotion, and gives you a tool with which to evaluate that intervention.

The Real Self: A Clinical Perspective

Because the term "self" has been used by so many theoreticians, it is necessary to define my use of it. Further, more detailed consideration can be found in *The Real Self.*[3.2]

First, a clinical description of a concept of the self:

Self-image consists of the image that an individual has of himself or herself at a particular time and in a particular situation. It consists of his or her body image and the mental representation of his or her state at that time. This image may be conscious or unconscious, realistic or distorted.

Self-representation, a more enduring schema than self-image, it is constructed by the ego out of the multitude of realistic and distorted self-images that an individual has had at different times. It represents the person as he or she consciously and unconsciously perceives himself or herself, and may be dormant or active.

Supraordinate self-organization refers to the fact that subjective experience may be organized by multiple self-representations, the "I" of one experience not necessarily being the same as the "I" of another experience. This term is used for the organization and patterning of the various subordinate self-images and -representations. It connects them, provides a continuity between them and the sense of unity and wholeness. This is one of the capacities that is pathologically impaired.

The Real Self: An Intrapsychic Object Relations Perspective

The real self consists of the sum total of the intrapsychic images of the self and its associated object representations. The term "real self" implies healthy, normal, with a very important conscious reality component, although there are inputs from both fantasy and the unconscious.

The real healthy self has two functions: It provides an emotional vehicle for self-expression, and it also operates to maintain self-esteem through the mastery of reality tasks.

Why the term "real self" rather than Winnicott's term the "true self"?[3.3] Winnicott's pioneering effort occurred before modern developmental studies had been carried out and was based on Freud's idea that there were two parts of the self: the part based on instincts, which was "true," and the part related to the environment or external world, which was false. Developmental studies have shown that this is a false dichotomy, since the self internalizes and integrates the early interactions with the mother and the external world to form an essential part of the self that is then also invested with both libidinal and aggressive drives of the instincts.

The term "real self" draws a sharp contrast to the false self of the disorders of the self. The false sense of self is not based on reality, but on a fantasy, and it maintains self-esteem not by efforts to master reality, but by defending against painful affects.

The real self consists of both the subordinate self-representations and the overriding supraordinate organization. This real self has its own development, its own capacities and functions, and its own psychopathology.

The Self and the Ego

The self and the ego develop and function as parallel partners; for example, like two horses in tandem in the same harness. The self is the representational arm of the ego, and the ego is the executive arm of the self, although each is more than that. If the ego is developmentally arrested, the self will also be developmentally arrested.

Erik Erikson referred to the dual and inseparable nature of the self ego as follows: "Ego identity refers to the ego's synthesizing power in the light of its central psychosocial function. Self identity to the integration of the individual's self role images. One speaks of self identity rather than ego identity when referring to the I perceiving itself as continuous in time and uniform in substance."

The self, of course, is mostly preconscious and conscious; the ego, through its synthesizing functions, is mostly unconscious. The ego's synthesizing function does for the psyche what respiration and circulation do for the soma.

Capacities of the Self

As the self goes through these stages and becomes whole and autonomous, it takes on all of these vital capacities or functions of the self: (1) The capacity for *spontaneity* and aliveness of affect. (2) The capacity for *self-entitlement*. From early experiences of mastery, coupled with parental acknowledgment and support of the emerging self, the sense builds up that the self is entitled to appropriate experiences of mastery and pleasure, as well as the environmental input necessary to achieve these objectives. This sense, of course, is severely deficient in borderline and schizoid patients and is pathologically inflated in the narcissistic disorder of the self. (3) The capacity for *self-activation, self-assertion, and self-support*. This is the capacity to identify one's unique individuated wishes and to use autonomous initiative and assertion to express them in reality and to support and defend them when under attack. Again, this is a capacity that is impaired in disorders of the self.

It's one thing to activate yourself and to do something; it's quite another to acknowledge to yourself that you have done it. And this is the next capacity. (4) The acknowledgment of self-activation and maintenance of self-esteem; that is, to identify and acknowledge to one's self that one's self, in both senses of the term, has coped with an affective state or an environmental issue or task in a positive, adaptive manner. This acknowledgment is the vehicle for autonomously fueling adequate self-esteem. (5) Soothing of painful affects. The capacity to autonomously devise means to limit, minimize, and soothe painful affects. (6) The continuity of the self, the acknowledgment that the "I" of one experience is continuous over time and related to the "I" of another experience. (7) The capacity for commitment—to commit the self to an objective or a relationship and to persevere, despite obstacles, to attain that goal. (8) The capacity for creativity—to use the self to change old familiar patterns into new, unique, and different patterns. (9) The capacity for intimacy—to express the self fully in a close relationship with minimal anxiety about abandonment or engulfment. (10) The capacity for autonomy to regulate affect and self-esteem freely and autonomously with minimal fear of abandonment or engulfment.

Further Development of the Self

The self doesn't cease to develop when it passes through the stages of separation-individuation, roughly at about ages 1½ to 3. Each later phase of development has its own input into the further development and maturation of the sense of self. This was illustrated by Erikson[3.1] in his discussion of the stages of development. Erikson described how the resolution of each psychosocial stage of development provided additional capacities for the self, such as industry, initiative and generativity. I will summarize these because the disorders of the self are developmentally arrested before these later stages.

The whole process of the development of the self culminates in the identity crisis of adolescence, where the adolescent must test, select, and integrate the self-images of childhood in light of the demands of adolescence and adulthood and sexual maturation. The final self is fixed at the end of adolescence as superordinate to any single identification from the individual's childhood.

Although it's fixed in terms of identification with childhood self-images, it still remains open to further development change.

Clinical Diagnosis by DSM-IV(1)

As pointed out in Chapter 2, the strength of the DSM-IV system is that since it is descriptive on the basis of symptoms (Table 3-1), it is based on the most obvious and, therefore, the most easily replicated phenomena. Thus, research studies will provide the greatest reliability. Also, since it's not based on any single theory, it can be used to test all theories. From a scientific point of view, however, it has been an obstacle to diagnosis of disorders of the self because, since it is based on symptoms, it is based on the most transient, most evanescent phenomena. Also, it seems to emphasize lower-level patients whose functioning is seriously impaired. This results in high-level patients often being diagnosed as neurotic. The limitations of Axis II in diagnosing personality disorders have been explored by Westen and Arkowitz-Westen.[3.3] They reported that 60% of patients who came to treatment with personality pathology were undiagnosable on Axis II.

TABLE 3-1.

The Personality Disorders (DSM-IV)

Listed below is a synopsis of the essential features of the eleven DSM-IV personality disorders to serve as a framework for illustrating the Masterson approach.

Cluster A

1. **Paranoid**
   suspicious, hypersensitive, restricted affect

2. **Schizoid**
   emotional coldness, indifference, no friends

3. **Schizotypal**
   magical thinking, ideas of reference, social isolation, recurrent illusions, odd speech, poor face-to-face rapport, suspicious, social anxiety

Cluster B

4. **Antisocial**
   juvenile delinquency, irresponsible, criminal activities, aggressiveness, financial difficulties, impulsivity, recklessness, lying

5. **Borderline**
   impulsivity, idealization/devaluation, anger, identity disturbance, affective instability, intolerance of being alone, self-damaging acts, chronic emptiness/boredom

6. **Histrionic**
   dramatic, vain, dependent

7. **Narcissistic**
   grandiose, preoccupied with fantasies, exhibitionistic, poor response to criticism, manipulative, exploitative

Cluster C

8. **Avoidant**
   rejection sensitive, shy, socially withdrawn, desires affection/acceptance, low self-esteem

9. **Dependent**
   dependent, subordinates own needs, lacks self-confidence

10. **Obsessive-compulsive**
    restricted affectivity, perfectionistic, stubborn, compulsive, indecisive

11. **Personality Disorder, Not Otherwise Specified**

Clinical Diagnosis by Developmental Self and Object Relations

The developmental self and object relations approach to diagnosis (see Table 3-2) divides those 11 categories into four: borderline personality disorders of the self, narcissistic disorder of the self, and antisocial and paranoid schizoid disorders.

Subcategories of borderline are dependent, passive–aggressive, compulsive, and histrionic. Each of these subcategories reflects a different style of defense against the abandonment depression.

The narcissistic personality disorder includes the exhibitionist and the closet or hidden narcissistic disorder, which is not recognized in DSM-IV, and the devaluing narcissistic disorder, also not recognized in DSM-IV.

The organizing concept of this psychodynamic diagnostic scheme is the way in which the self-representation relates to the object-representation. In the borderline disorder of the self, the self relates to the object by either clinging, distancing, or acting out. In the narcissistic disorder, either the object-representation co-ops the self or the self-representation co-ops the object-representation, or they both are extruded, projected, and acted out.

The antisocial personality has completely detached the relationship between the self and the object. In the paranoid disorders, the object is projected to protect the self. In the schizoid disorder, the self distances from the object, and in the avoidant, which is similar to the schizoid, there is massive avoidance. The schizotypal is very close to schizophrenia.

All of these disorders of the self have impaired capacities of the self and developmental arrest of the ego so that this feature in itself does not distinguish among them. To do that, we must focus on the intrapsychic structure.

Differential Diagnosis by Intrapsychic Structure

Object relations theory is the psychoanalytic study of the internalization of early relationships, mostly with the mother, and later with the father. The vocabulary of object relations theory consists of self- and

TABLE 3-2.

The Developmental Self and Object Relations Approach to Disorders of the Self: The Masterson Approach

1. Borderline Personality Disorders

- a. Dependent
- b. Passive-aggressive
- c. Compulsive
- d. Histrionic

2. Narcissistic Personality Disorder

- a. Exhibitionistic
  - Higher level
  - Middle level
  - Lower level
- b. Closet
  - Higher level
  - Middle level
  - Lower level
- c. Devaluer

3. The Antisocial

4. Paranoid Schizoid Disorders

- a. Paranoid
- b. Schizoid
  - 1. Avoidant
  - 2. Closet
- c. Schizotypal

object-representations and the affects that link them, as well as ego functions and defenses. For example, the child has an interaction with the mother. The self-representation of that interaction, the object-representation of that interaction, and the affect that links the two are internalized to form the split object-relations unit.

Borderline Disorders of the Self

Figure 3-1 shows the split object-relations unit of the borderline personality disorder. You will note that it consists of two circles, one on each side. This split-object relations unit consists of two part-units, each of which has of a self-representation at the bottom and an object-representation at the top linked by an affect.

There is a self-representation of being the good passive child, an object-representation that offers approval for regressive and clinging behavior, and the affect that links the two, depending on what perspective is used to describe it: as feeling good, as being taken care of, as being loved, as being fed, or as gratifying the wish for reunion. This part-unit is one of the two major psychic states of the borderline personality disorder.

Withdrawing or Aggressive Part-Unit

The maternal part object withdraws, and is angry at and critical of efforts toward separation-individuation. In this part-unit, the part self-representation is of being inadequate, bad, ugly, and causing that withdrawal. The most important part of this withdrawing unit is the affect that links the two representations, which I have called the abandonment depression.

Abandonment Depression

The affect is more intense than a midlife depression. At the time that the development arrest occurs, the child feels a loss of the mother's support as a loss of part of himself or herself. So the patient will express this as a loss of something vital: the loss of blood, the loss of oxygen, or the loss of vital body parts. Thus, this crucial abandonment depression is no single affect, but a complex of six affects: homicidal rage, suicidal depression, panic helplessness and hopelessness, emptiness, void, and guilt.

Splitting Defense

The other part-unit, on the right, is called the withdrawing or aggressive part-unit. These two part-units are kept apart by the splitting

THE MASTERSON INSTITUTE

Borderline Diagnosis Criteria for Borderline Personality Disorder DSM-IV

A pervasive pattern of instability of interpersonal relationships, self-image, and affects, and marked impulsivity beginning by early adulthood and present in a variety of contexts, as indicated by five (or more) of the following:

1. frantic efforts to avoid real or imagined abandonment
2. a pattern of unstable and intense interpersonal relationships characterized by alternating between extremes of idealization and devaluation
3. identity disturbance: markedly and persistently unstable self-image or sense of self-image or sense of self
4. impulsivity in at least two areas that are potentially self-damaging
5. recurrent suicidal behavior, gestures or threats, or self-mutilating behavior
6. affective instability due to a marked reactivity of mood (e.g., intense dysphoria, irritability, or anxiety usually lasting a few hours and only rarely more than a few days)
7. chronic feelings of emptiness
8. inappropriate, intense anger or difficulty controlling anger (e.g., frequent displays of temper, constant anger, recurrent physical fights)
9. transient, stress-related paranoid ideation or severe dissociative symptoms

---

SPLIT OBJECT RELATIONS UNIT OF THE BORDERLINE

SPLITTING DEFENSE

REWARDING OR LIBIDINAL PART-UNIT (RORU)

Part-Object Representation:

a maternal part-object Which offers approval of regressive and clinging behavior

AFFECT

feeling good
being taken care of
being loved
being fed
gratifying the wish for reunion

Part Self Representation:

a part self-representation of being the good, passive child—unique and special/ grandiose

WITHDRAWING OR AGGRESSIVE PART-UNIT (WORU)

Part-Object Representation:

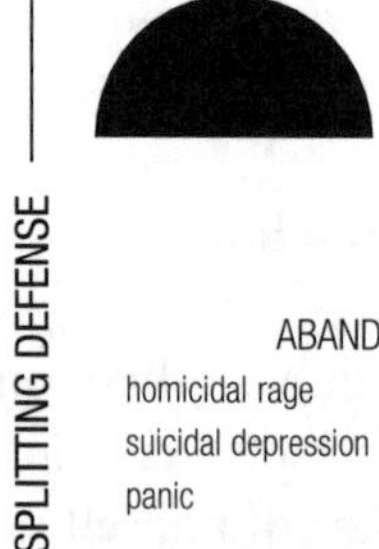

a maternal part-object which withdraws, is angry and critical of efforts toward separation- individuation

AFFECT

ABANDONMENT DEPRESSION

homicidal rage
suicidal depression
panic
hopelessness and helplessness
emptiness and void
guilt

Part Self Representation:

a part self-representation of being inadequate, bad, ugly, and insect, etc.

Developmental Arrest of the Ego:

Ego Defects—poor reality perception; frustration tolerance; impulse control; ego boundaries.
Primitive Ego Defense Mechanisms—splitting; acting-out; clinging, avoidance, denial; projection; projective identification.
Split Ego—reality ego plus pathologic (or pleasure) ego.

Figure 3-1

mechanism of defense. This mechanism keeps mutually contradictory affective states separated from each other; they remain conscious, but they do not influence one another. It also keeps separate the self and object-representations associated with these states.

Developmental Arrest of the Ego and the Self

The developmental arrest of the ego leads to defects in ego functions: poor reality perception, impulse control, frustration tolerance, and ego boundaries, and primitive mechanisms of defense—splitting, acting out, clinging, avoidance, denial, projection, and projective identification. The developmental arrest of the self produces impairments in all the capacities of the self.

Split Ego

The ego structure itself is split into two parts. One part functions according to the reality principle, in other words, sees the reality as it is and tries to deal with it. The other functions according to the pleasure principle to pursue what feels good regardless of whether or not it's real.

The child's ego initially operates on the pleasure principle, but as Freud taught us, the pleasure principle comes up against reality and gives way to the reality principle. In these patients, this transformation occurs only partially, so that a fairly large part of their ego structure functions according to the pleasure principle. In the borderline patient, this is called the pathological ego. It allows borderline patients gratification through fantasy that would not be possible for someone who had a more reality-based ego.

Clinical Function of Borderline Object Relations Unit Disorders-of-the-Self Triad

This intrapsychic structure is in place between ages 2 and 3. After that time, any later-life separation or efforts to self-activate trigger the withdrawing unit with its abandonment depression. This, in turn, activates the disorders-of-the-self triad—self-activation leads to anxiety and depression, which lead to defense. This applies not just to actions, but also to individuative thoughts.

What happens either as a result of a separation stress or of self-activation? The withdrawing unit, with its abandonment depression, is activated, or precipitated. Once the patient begins to feel the abandonment depression, he or she has three options for defense. Option 1 is to activate the rewarding unit. When the rewarding unit is activated, the patient gives up self-activation. But since the patient is able to deny the self-destructive aspects of giving up self-activation, he or she is able to feel good under the operation of the rewarding unit pathological ego alliance, and the abandonment depression subsides. In the work, you would see the clinging defense as the patient projected the rewarding object onto the therapist and clings; then the depression subsides, and the patient feels fine and is found to be acting in a self-destructive manner.

Option 2 is to distance from the withdrawing object by detaching affect. Option 3 is to massively project the withdrawing unit and act it out.

The borderline patient truly has a Hobson's choice. Either the patient feels bad and abandoned (the withdrawing unit), or defends against that unit at the cost of adaptation to reality, which the patient is able, however, to deny. That is the issue that must be dealt with by therapeutic interventions. In clinical work with borderline personality disorders of the self, one is always working with the abandonment depression and/or some defense against it.

The Narcissistic Disorder of the Self

The intrapsychic structure of the narcissistic personality disorder of the self (see Figure 3-2) shares similarities with the borderline. There are two self- and object-representations, kept apart by the splitting defense. There are also profound differences. First, these self- and object-representations are fused, not separate. There are two part-units, one of which we call the grandiose self-defensive fused part-unit (on the left) and the harsh, aggressive, attacking part-unit (on the right). For the narcissistic disorder, these are analogous to the rewarding and withdrawing part-units of the borderline.

The grandiose self-defensive fused part-unit of the narcissistic disorder consists of a self-representation, which is grandiose, and an object-

THE MASTERSON INSTITUTE

Narcissistic Personality Disorder Diagnosis Criteria DSM-IV

A pervasive pattern of grandiosity (in fantasy or behavior), need for admiration, and lack of empathy, beginning by early adulthood and present in a variety of contexts, as indicated by five (or more) of the following:

1. has a grandiose sense of self-importance (e.g., exaggerates achievements and talents, expects to be recognized as superior without commensurate achievements)
2. is preoccupied with fantasies of unlimited success, power, brilliance, beauty, or ideal love
3. believes that he or she is "special" and unique and can only be understood by, or should associate with, other special or high-status people (or institutions)
4. requires excessive admiration
5. has a sense of entitlement, i.e., unreasonable expectations or especially favorable treatment or automatic compliance with his or her expectations
6. is interpersonally exploitive, i.e., takes advantage of others to achieve his or her own ends
7. lacks empathy: is unwilling to recognize or identify with the feelings and needs of others
8. is often envious of others or believes that others are envious of him or her
9. shows arrogant, haughty behaviors or attitudes

SPLIT OBJECT RELATIONS UNIT OF THE NARCISSISTIC PERSONALITY DISORDER

DEFENSIVE FUSED PART-UNIT

OBJECT (omnipotent)

SELF (grandiose)

SPLITTING DEFENSE

AGGRESSIVE FUSED PART-UNIT

OBJECT (harsh, attacking, devaluing)

SELF (inadequate, fragmented unworthy, unentitled)

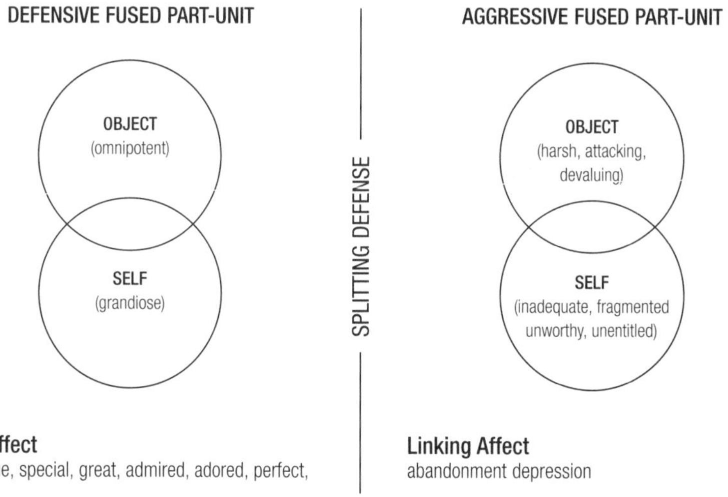

Linking Affect
being unique, special, great, admired, adored, perfect, entitled

Linking Affect
abandonment depression

Ego Functions
poor reality perception, impulse control, frustration tolerance, ego boundaries.

Ego Defense Mechanisms
splitting, avoidance, denial, acting-out, clinging, projection, projective identification.

Figure 3-2

representation, which is omnipotent. The affect that links them is a feeling of being unique, special, great, admired, adored, perfect, and entitled. The aggressive fused part-unit consists of an object-representation that is harsh and attacking, a self-representation of being inadequate and fragmented, and a linking affect of abandonment defense.

How does this system operate? It operates according to the same principle as does the disorders-of-the-self triad: self-activation leads to anxiety and depression, which lead to defense.

What triggers this harsh, aggressive underlying unit is either separation stress, self-activation, or failures in empathy. When this part-unit is triggered, the narcissistic patient has three defensive alternatives. If the maximum investment is in the grandiose self, the patient will activate the grandiose self and present the grandiose self to be admired and adored—and the harsh aggressive unit subsides. This is the most common form of defense and what most people consider to be the entire range of the narcissistic disorder, that is, the exhibitionistic type. If the patient's major investment is in the object-representation rather than in the self-representation, the patient defends by idealizing others, including the therapist. The grandiosity is gratified by basking in the glow of the object's idealized omnipotence and perfection. I call this the closet narcissistic disorder of the self.

Fortunately for therapists, these are the two major defensive forms seen clinically. There is another form, however, that is more difficult for therapists to manage, which I call the devaluing narcissistic disorder. This patient doesn't activate either of the above styles of defense, but rather projects and acts out the underlying harsh aggressive unit. Those stimuli, self-activation and separation stress, which in the other two types would activate either the grandiose self or the omnipotent object of the grandiose self-defensive unit, instead activate the underlying aggressive unit and the patient projects the inadequate self on the therapist and plays out the role of the attacking object by devaluing and attacking the therapist to restore intrapsychic equilibrium.

The Schizoid Disorder of the Self

The schizoid disorder of the self (see Figure 3-3) has the same two-part intrapsychic structure kept apart by the splitting defense with a self-representation and an object-representation on either side. The

Schizoid Personality Disorder Diagnosis Criteria
DSM-IV

A. A pervasive pattern of detachment from social relationships and a restricted range of expression of emotions in interpersonal settings, beginning in early adulthood and present in a variety of contexts, as indicated by four (or more) of the following:

1. neither desires nor enjoys close relationships, including being part of a family
2. almost always chooses solitary activities
3. has little, if any, interest in having sexual experiences with another person
4. takes pleasure in few, if any, activities
5. lacks close friends or confidants other than first-degree relatives
6. appears indifferent to the praise of criticism of others
7. shows emotional coldness, detachment, or flattened affectivity

B. Does not occur exclusively during the course of Schizophrenia, a Mood Disorder With Psychotic Features, another Psychotic Disorder, or a Pervasive Developmental Disorder and is not due to the direct psysiological effects of a general medical condition.

SPLIT OBJECT RELATIONS UNIT OF THE SCHIZOID DISORDER OF THE SELF

SPLITTING DEFENSE

MASTER SLAVE PART-UNIT

Part-Object Representation:

a maternal part-object which is manipulative, coercive, is the master and wants only to use, not relate to

AFFECT

In Jail, but connected, existence acknowledged, relief in not being alienated.

Part Self Representation:

a part self-representation of a dependent, a slave who provided a function for the object and is a victim

SADISTIC OBJECT – SELF IN EXILE PART-UNIT

Part-Object Representation:

a maternal part-object which is sadistic, dangerous, devaluing, depriving, abandoning

AFFECT

ABANDONMENT DEPRESSION

Depression, rage, loneliness, fear of cosmic aloneness, despair

Part Self Representation:

a part self-representation of being alienated, in exile, isolated but self-contained to self-reliant

Developmental Arrest of the Ego:

Ego Defects—poor reality perception; frustration tolerance; impulse control; ego boundaries.
Primitive Ego Defense Mechanisms—splitting; acting-out; clinging, avoidance, denial; projection; projective identification, use of fantasy to substitute for real relationships and self reliance.
Split Ego—reality ego plus pathologic (or pleasure) ego.

Figure 3-3

defensive part-unit is called the master–slave unit and the other unit is called the sadistic object self-in-exile unit.

The defensive master–slave unit has an object representation that is manipulative and coercive, one that is the master and wants only to use, not relate to. The self-representation is of a dependent, a slave who provides a function for the object and is a victim. The affect that links these two is that of being in jail, but at least connected; existence acknowledged, a sense of relief at not being alienated.

The sadistic object self-in-exile has an object-representation that is sadistic, manipulating, hostile, attacking, and using, and a part self-representation of being alienated and isolated, but self-contained. The affect that links these is that of the abandonment depression, with some very important additions: the sense of alienation, because of the lack of a positive connection with the object, and the fear of being so alienated that the person cannot come back and make any contact at all. This fear is often expressed in a metaphor from outer-space exploration: the astronaut is tied to the capsule by a rope, the rope is severed, and the astronaut floats off into the void, totally alienated.

The ego functions of the schizoid patient have several important aspects. The schizoid patient's conception is that there is no pathway to gratification with objects at all. Therefore, the person develops what looks like self-sufficiency but really is a pseudo self-sufficiency, a defensive self-sufficiency.

In addition, schizoid patients have a reputation in the literature of not wishing to relate to the object. This is not true. Rather, it is therapist's countertransference reaction to their detachment and distancing. They do want to relate, but they are so terrified of what will happen (i.e., that it will trigger the sadistic object) that they evoke the massive distancing defense.

How do schizoid patients' defensive systems operate? Separation stress or self-activation moves toward sharing or closeness and triggers the underlying sadistic object self in exile, and they become detached and move further into an alienated state. When that becomes intolerable, they then move back toward the master–slave unit, and we call this back-and-forth movement the schizoid compromise! Not too close and not too far. Too close means being a slave, and too far means being alienated, out in the void.

Chapter Four

Differential Diagnosis

Between Personality Disorders and Other Disorders

The Developmental Self and Object Relations Approach

This approach to differential diagnosis has several advantages. For instance, it integrates the developmental with both object relations theory and a theory of the self. Also, it emphasizes the least episodic, most enduring, aspect of the personality disorder, that is, the fixated intrapsychic structure (self- and object-representations, ego functions, and defense mechanisms). Moreover, it provides clinical tools for hypothesis testing and validation. And, finally, it makes the clinical evaluation of diagnosis an active, dynamic live process.

Features of the Clinical Interview

Evaluation begins with the initial encounter when the therapist obtains the data or evidence to make the diagnosis. It's important to be sure that the theory fits the patient and not to tailor the patient to fit the theory. The theory deepens the meaning of clinical evidence and enables the therapist to pose hypotheses to be explored and tested.

The therapist allows the patient to tell his or her story, and where necessary, begins to ask questions to fill in what has been left out. The therapist is attempting to evaluate not just symptomatology or pathology, but also the patient's ego strength, that which the therapist will lean on in conducting the therapy. Ego strength can be seen in early developmental history in the ability to perform in school and social relationships and in various hobbies. The theory also provides guidance on what to look for; for example, one looks for separation anxiety in early development, as well as in the history of the present illness.

The precipitating stress for the present illness is an important finding. In other words, why did the patient come now rather than six months earlier or six months later? This often provides a wealth of critical information. What is generally involved is a separation-individuation stress. There are certain nodal points in development that require an increased capacity for self-activation that can be precipitating stresses for these patients. It begins with the child's move from home to the school, from the local grammar school to the junior high school, to the senior high school, graduating from high school and going to college, setting out on a career, and so forth. It's important for the therapist to take responsibility for ferreting out this information, because the patient more than likely is unaware of the profound significance of this separation-individuation stress.

The interview probably begins with the DSM-IV symptoms that the patient presents. The therapist then looks for a separation-individuation stress, and follows this up to evaluate the intrapsychic structure, the strength of the ego, the ego defense mechanisms, the ego functions, and the impairment of the capacities of the self. This is a process during which the therapist develops hypotheses from what he or she has heard, and pursues the lead, if information is not given. This may involve trying out various therapeutic interventions to test various hypotheses. It is well worth taking the time to make the definitive diagnosis since the diagnosis is so important in determining therapeutic interventions.

Differential Diagnosis Between Disorders of the Self and Other Disorders

The Affective Disorders

The affective disorders are believed to be genetic and they require pharmacotherapy. To establish the diagnosis, there is often a family history of affective disorder; thoughts, feelings, and actions, whether elevated or depressed, go in the same direction. Also, the affective depression is indicated by vegetative signs: anorexia and weight loss, insomnia, difficulty in concentration, psychomotor agitation, retardation fatigue and loss of energy. There are biological markers, such as the dexamethazone suppression test or REM sleep. Neither of these, however, is found positive in a high enough percentage of patients to be relied upon as a diagnostic too!.

In clinical studies,[4.1] patients with affective disorders have been found to have a very low incidence of borderline personality disorder, whereas for the borderline personality disorder, there is a somewhat higher incidence of comorbid affective depression disorder. Substance abuse and antisocial behavior more commonly characterize the family histories of borderline patients. Borderline patients also have a higher incidence of parental loss before age 6, and greater sensitivity to separation stress; often both parents are emotionally disturbed and the families are less organized, with more hostile conflict and more physical and sexual abuse. The borderline depression also differs in that it has qualities of emptiness, helplessness, hopelessness, and feelings of abandonment, which tend not to be present in the affective disorder depression.

The differentiation is crucial, since borderline depression ordinarily requires psychotherapy and the affective disorder depression requires medication. When both conditions are present, they should receive both psychotherapy and medication.

Schizophrenia and Psychosis

These most commonly become clinical issues with lower-level borderline patients who have a low functional level, and as such appear to be developmental neighbors of those with schizophrenic conditions that may be psychodynamically caused. The schizophrenic patient is unable to separate and pays the price for that by having poor ego boundaries, with the presence of delusions, hallucinations, disorganized speech, and flattening of affect, whereas a borderline is able to separate partially and gets the benefits of that separation of firmer ego boundaries, so that psychosis usually occurs under separation stress and is, therefore, a separation psychosis. It is very often precipitated by alcohol or drugs. In the psychosis, the patient may have paranoid projections, feelings of unreality, even delusions and hallucinations. If the patient is hospitalized, one can often differentiate a separation psychosis from a schizophrenic psychosis by the fact that even without medication, the borderline patient's psychosis will remit simply because the hospitalization overcomes the separation stress and restores the patient's borderline defenses.

Psychoneurosis

The psychoneurotic patient has passed through the stages of separation–individuation, past the preoedipal stage to the oedipal stage. As such, the patient has the capacity for whole self- and whole object-relations, and repression has replaced splitting. From the perspective of the personality disorder, to be psychoneurotic is an achievement. The psychoneurotic's higher-level intrapsychic structure, which consists of a whole object-representation and a whole self-representation, is reflected clinically in the fact that the patient has the capacity for a therapeutic alliance at the outset of treatment so that therapist and patient can work together on the problem. The clinical problem is that too often high-functioning patients with personality disorders are misdiagnosed as psychoneurotics and receive classical psychoanalysis with its emphasis on interpretation of transference, which does not do the job. The ultimate test of the diagnosis is that when one makes an interpretation, it is responded to in terms of oedipal conflict, not preoedipal conflict.

Substance Abuse

Substance abuse—alcohol or drugs—is so common among personality disorders as a defense that the therapist must take the initiative to explore or rule out its presence. Often the patient is either reluctant to report it or avoids reporting it: It has a devastating effect on the course of treatment, and it has to be taken into consideration from the outset. Substance abuse competes with therapy as a way of managing the patient's emotions.

Posttraumatic Stress Disorder

The clinician must be alert to the possibility of posttraumatic stress disorder (PTSD) because often the patient may be unaware of its presence or not recall it. The disorder occurs when the patient has experienced or witnessed an event that actually threatens death or serious injury or is a threat to the physical integrity of the person or someone close, and is associated with fear and helplessness. In PTSD, the event is reexperienced by (1) recurrent intrusive painful memories, (2) recurrent dreams, (3) memory flashbacks, and (4) intense physical or psychological distress at internal or external stimuli that symbolize the trauma or avoidance of stimuli associated with the trauma or the numbing of feelings: avoiding thoughts, feelings, or conversations associated with trauma; avoiding activities or places or memories. This may be associated with feelings of detachment, estrangement, and restriction of affect, or its opposite, symptoms of increased arousal, difficulty in sleeping, irritability, or hypervigilance.

Attention-Deficit/Hyperactivity Disorder

To be diagnosed with attention-deficit/hyperactivity disorder (ADHD), the patient must have six or more of the symptoms of an attention difficulty that have persisted for at least six months: fails to give close attention to details or makes careless mistakes, has difficulty sustaining attention in tasks or play activities, doesn't seem to listen when spoken to, doesn't follow through, has difficulty organizing activities, and so on. Hyperactivity, such as fidgeting of hands or feet, may occur in the classroom and other situations where one should remain seated. The patient has difficulty in playing or engaging in leisurely activities quietly, is often on the go, and talks incessantly. To this can be added impulsivity, blurting out answers before questions have been completed, difficulty in waiting his or her turn, interrupting or intruding on others.

Formerly considered a syndrome affecting only children and adolescents, it is now believed that in half of the cases arising in childhood/adolescence, the individuals do not grow out of it. Thus, it then becomes an issue for adult patients, as well, manifesting in such symptoms as drinking and seemingly antisocial behavior. There is also usually a history of being relegated to special education or having difficulties in school and of being held back. The patients present as constantly forgetting, misplacing things, procrastinating, having no attention span, and only half-finishing projects. It is, of course, important to differentiate these patients from borderline patients, who can have the same symptoms. There is a theory that ADHD by itself, because of the cognitive difficulties it produces, can result in a borderline personality disorder. This is yet to be validated in research where you would have to see a child with ADHD who had a good-enough mother but who nevertheless later developed a borderline personality disorder. The differential diagnosis can be made by considering the history from childhood plus using a standard screening questionnaire, noting the patient's failure to respond to confrontation, and finally, his or her response to medication, such as Ritalin.

Differential Diagnosis Between the Disorders of the Self

Exhibitionistic Narcissistic Disorder of the Self

In the ordinary case, the disorder is not difficult to diagnose according to the following: (1) DSM-IV symptoms, (2) intrapsychic structure, (3) clinical features.

Antisocial Disorders of the Self

The clinical picture involves the inability to conform to social norms: performing antisocial acts; deceitfulness, such as lying or conning others; impulsivity or failure to plan ahead; irritability and aggressiveness; disregard of self and others; consistent irresponsibility; lack of guilt or remorse. The DSM stresses that the patient must be at least 18 years of age, although our clinical work indicates that a psychopathic personality can be genetic and can appear long before 18 years of age, and it is vital for the person working with personality disorders to be alert to this condition. I have done a number of consultations where the therapist was concerned about his or her therapeutic technique when the issue was that the therapist had misdiagnosed a patient who was psychopathic as having a narcissistic or borderline disorder.

We used to be taught that patients with antisocial disorders do not experience anxiety or depression, but they do so when they are trapped in a situation from which they cannot escape by acting out. In addition, they can mimic treatment for long periods to achieve psychopathic secondary gain. The diagnosis is made by confrontation where the patient responds by projection and acting out. From a theoretical psychodynamic point of view, the psychopathic patient has separated from the object by cutting off all affective contact with the object. Since this emotional link between the self and object is the basis of our psychotherapy, the psychopath who has cut the link is not amenable to this form of psychotherapy.

However, Samenow[4.2] reports results with a cognitive psychotherapy that focuses on the patient's thinking styles.

The diagnosis can be illustrated by a vignette. I examined a 15-year-old boy who, during a robbery, shot and killed a woman and her 3-year-old daughter. When I examined him, in front of a group, he was delighted, enjoying himself as the center of attention, and was quite cooperative. Near the end of the session, I said to him, "There is something perhaps you can clarify for me. You tell me that you're sorry to have killed that mother and daughter. On the other hand, I hear that on the floor, when you are angry at a nurse, you draw a picture with a knife through her heart, or when you are angry with one of your peers, you make a motion with your fingers of shooting the person. What I don't understand is how, if you are really sorry, you can make fun of killing, and if you're making fun of killing, I wonder if you are really sorry."

The eager-to-please deportment disappeared, and a curtain came over his facial expression. He stared at me wordless for four or five minutes, and I thanked him for coming in. He left, and when he got to his room, he had a fit of rage and destroyed the furniture. Diagnosis: reaction to confrontation, projection acting out, psychopathic personality.

Paranoid Personality

The clinical picture of paranoid personality consists of suspiciousness, feelings of being persecuted, and grandiosity. There is a pervasive split between the outer and inner worlds involving (1) self, (2) object, (3) affects, (4) morality, (5) sexuality, and (6) cognitive style. The outer world: demanding, arrogant, mistrustful, driven, unromantic, monolithic, vigilant. The inner world: frightened, timid, self-doubting, gullible, inconsiderate, vulnerable to emotions, unable to grasp the totality of actual events. The patient is projecting the object-representation externally.

Schizotypal Disorders of the Self

In the schizotypal disorder, there are an impaired capacity for close relationships and both cognitive and perceptual distortions.

To summarize, in taking a developmental object relations approach to diagnosis, begin with the symptoms, look for the separation stress, the defects in ego functioning and the primitive mechanisms of defense, and the impairments of the self, and when that information has been obtained, sketch out the intrapyschic object relations units according to the way the patient relates. Therapeutic interventions are then used to confirm the diagnosis.

Chapter Five

Differential Diagnosis

Defensive Focus on the Object

The four disorders of the self are listed together here because the main theme of their clinical presentation is their need to focus on the object as a way of regulating the self. Thus, their superficial clinical presentations are so similar that they can present a difficult problem in differential diagnosis.

1. The closet narcissistic disorder of the self
2. The devaluing narcissistic disorder of the self
3. The borderline disorder of the self (distancing)
4. The schizoid disorder of the self

The DSM-IV symptoms and intrapsychic structures and transference acting out of these four disorders were outlined in Chapter 3 and some additional differentiating features are described in the following.

Disorders of the Self

Closet Narcissistic Disorder of the Self

This disorder creates the biggest diagnostic difficulty because the patient's clinical picture appears to be like that of the borderline. The patient is focusing on the therapist. The patient goes through the triad of experiencing self-activation, which leads to depression, which leads to defense, as with the borderline. However, the borderline's defense is clinging whereas the closet narcissistic defense is fusing with the therapist in a fused self/object representation. The patient projects the idealized object onto the therapist, idealizes the therapist, and gets his or her grandiosity gratified by glowing in the perfection of the object. It is common for therapists to misdiagnose this as a borderline disorder and then use confrontation, which impels the patient to become angry and attack the therapist. Or some patients may seem to respond to confrontation, which would further confuse the diagnosis by seemingly confirming that the patient has a borderline disorder of the self. However, the therapist will note that there is no increase in affect, so what the therapist is seeing is not a change, but defensive compliance.

The therapist then begins to think in terms of "these difficult-to-treat borderline patients," not recognizing that the diagnosis is wrong. It's necessary for the therapist to take a step back, reevaluate the diagnosis, and shift the therapeutic intervention accordingly to mirroring interpretation of narcissistic vulnerability. Integration of this intevention confirms the diagnosis.

Devaluing Narcissistic Disorder

Most of the narcissistic disorders use as a defense the grandiose self-, omnipotent object-representation. This disorder, however, operates in the reverse fashion. When exposed to empathy failure or separation stress and the need for self-activation, these patients do not activate the grandiose self omnipotent object, but instead activate the underlying harsh unit and project the impaired, flawed self onto the therapist, and act out the role of the attacking object. It's important for the therapist to realize that this behavior serves the same function as does the exhibiting defense of the exhibitionist or the idealizing defense of the closet narcissistic disorder, and must be interpreted as such. Patients with this disorder are particularly prone to countertransference reactions on the part of therapists who are being attacked.

Borderline Disorder of the Self (Distancing)

This patient appears to have no emotional need for others and to function effectively and to be unaware of his or her own needs. The disorder has to be differentiated from the schizoid and detached closet narcissistic disorders. The key difference is the response to confrontation.

Schizoid Disorders of the Self

The purest cluster of the schizoid is represented by the patient who shows withdrawal, introversion, and lack of affect. There also is pseudo self-sufficiency and a rich fantasy life that substitute for relationships. Although that is the pure cluster, there are two others: the patient exhibits a narcissistic defense which is basically to distance by being above others, or a borderline defense, which is to distance from others by being below others.

The Differential Diagnosis: Distancing Borderline, Detached Closet Narcissistic, and Schizoid

The abandonment depression is experienced by the distancing borderline patient as loss of the object, by the detached closet narcissistic patient as fragmentation of the self, and by the schizoid patient as alienation of the self. In the transference acting out, the borderline patient is distancing without much affect. The narcissistic patient is idealizing, fusing, and imagining that the therapist knows things the patient hasn't reported, and focusing intensely on the therapist. The schizoid patient is detached, distancing with intense private fantasies. Clinical depression may or may not be present in the distancing borderline patient, is present in the closset narcissistic disorder, and is not found in the schizoid disorder. Envy is not a characteristic of the borderline or schizoid disorder but is present in the narcissistic disorders. The ultimate test is the response to intervention, and if it appears that one intervention isn't working, it is necessary to shift to others until the person's response confirms the diagnosis.

One has to be aware that the closet narcissistic patient and the schizoid patient may appear to be responding to confrontation, thus confirming the diagnosis of borderline disorder. However, a careful review will show that the response is attributable to defensive compliance rather than to integration because there is no increase in affect.

The following cases illustrate the steps the therapist must take before arriving at a final diagnosis. It is legitimate to start with your best clinical impression and then follow the patient's response because, in the final analysis, the ultimate confirmation of the diagnosis is the patient's response to the therapeutic intervention.

CASE 1:

SEXUAL ACTING OUT AS A DEFENSE AGAINST INTIMACY: Distancing Borderline or Secret Schizoid Disorder*

Chief Complaint

Ms. C. began her initial session in a bland, breezy, friendly manner with only the slightest hint of breathlessness betraying that she might be feeling anxiety. She was diminutive and childlike, although her dress was appropriate for her age and professional status. Ms. C. is single, white, has an advanced degree in her field, and is employed as a highly paid professional in a competitive, "cut-throat" occupation.

Ms. C. entered twice-a-week therapy with me after a six-month hiatus from her previous therapist. As the first session progressed, so did the severity of the reasons she gave for resuming therapy. First, she noted that she "realized the benefits of seeing somebody in therapy" and that she "just needed someone impartial to talk to." Next, Ms. C. reported a "self-esteem" problem that surfaced mostly in relationships with men.

She revealed that she was still recovering from a depression after separating 10 months earlier from a man with whom she had lived for

*Case courtesy of Barbara L. Short, Ph.D.

approximately 18 months—the longest relationship in her life. She described this as having been an emotionally abusive relationship and her depression as having been so severe that her therapist referred her to a psychiatrist for medication. Although she was able to continue work during the worst two or three months of her depression, she had most of the symptoms of a mild major depressive episode. She took Paxil for four months but said that she didn't feel it helped much.

She maintained that she never wanted to have another abusive relationship, but probably would. She said that it seemed beyond her control: "I'm attracted to men for the wrong reason. It's a chemical thing. If the sex is good, I get hooked. I want to find out why this is happening. Sometimes I don't feel it's emotionally healthy." Ms. C. then reluctantly revealed that she had another kind of problem with sex, saying, "I want some kind of attention, but then I sleep with strangers, and when they leave, I feel like dirt." She said she would like to get married and have children, but felt "a little panicky" that time was passing, and she had less and less hope that this would ever happen.

Finally, when she went out with men, Ms. C. said, she often drank alcohol to excess, and sometimes used illegal drugs, such as marijuana and cocaine. However, she did not appear to be addicted to these substances. Rather, it appeared that she used them quite specifically as adjuncts to her sexual behavior.

History of Present Illness

Ms. C. said that although she had felt lonely and depressed since early childhood, her first identifiable depressive episode occurred at age 32 when she left the boyfriend with whom she had been living for 18 months. She was able to continue working, but for several months, she experienced sleep and appetite disturbance, extreme fatigue and lethargy, and difficulty concentrating. She reported that during these months, she "felt like I was dead, and wished I could die. It was frightening. I never want to go through something like that again." She stopped seeing her therapist (a marriage and family therapist who had been seeing her and her boyfriend as a couple) because she believed that the therapist had taken sides with her boyfriend and against her. The boyfriend continued in individual therapy, and Ms. C. did not seek additional therapy for about six months, at which time her physician referred her to me.

Ms. C. excelled in school and later in her profession. However, her social life has been characterized by superficial interpersonal relationships, usually of brief duration, extensive sexual acting out, and frequent excessive use of illegal drugs and alcohol.

Family History

Ms. C.'s mother was a nurse, and her father worked as a manager at a large corporation until Ms. C. was 15 years old. Ms. C. initially described her mother as a good mother who worked very hard. Later it emerged that their relationship was one of emotional uninvolvement and physical distance. The mother stayed long hours at work, and was seldom available for any activities with Ms. C. or her brother. Ms. C.'s memory of her mother is remarkable for its paucity of contact. It is largely limited to the lack of communication in the family: admonishments not to talk about feelings, not to feel sorry for herself, not to complain when she was so lucky to have so much, and so on. When Ms. C. had difficulties in high school, her mother's response was not to talk about them, but to ground her—confine her to her room after dinner for "months on end." Ms. C. said, "Being at home was like being in jail."

Ms. C. believes she had a "warm, close" relationship with her father until she was about 12, although she does not remember many specific events. She believes he became less involved in her life when she entered her teens. She did not know what happened, he "just seemed to disappear." He occasionally drank to excess, but not on a regular basis, and does not appear to have been an alcoholic. After he lost his mid-level managerial position when Ms. C. was 15, no other job was available, and he failed at several attempts to start his own businesses. He left home for two years to try to find work elsewhere, but was unsuccessful. He appears to have been a rather passive, ineffectual husband and father, and there is reason to suspect that his relationship with Ms. C. may have been overinvolved, if not actually sexual.

Ms. C.'s brother, 5 years older than she, was slightly mentally handicapped due to oxygen deprivation at birth. She said she believed that her mother felt responsible, and "never really got over it." As a result, and because she had good social skills and was very bright, her parents evidently felt Ms. C. could fend for herself, and gave her brother what little parental care was available. She was told that her brother "adored her," and she recalled that they shared a room during her early childhood.

Past History

Ms. C. was left alone a great deal as a child. She was sent to day care at the age of 6 months, and noted, "That's really all I've ever known." On the other hand, she also remembered having a warm, close relationship with her father. She described him as having been "very physical; hugging, holding me on his lap, and hand holding a lot—lots of physical affection." She also described herself as having been a bad girl all her life, as evidenced by her getting caught printing pages and pages of "dirty" words in the first grade, and as being lonely and depressed from her earliest years.

She recalled one traumatic event at the age of 7 when she was almost abducted by a man in a car who picked her up, took her into some nearby woods, and kissed her before releasing her and driving off when he saw her mother running toward them. She remembered being frightened, but that it was never talked about, even on the day it occurred. When she tried to talk to her mother about it, she was told to never mention it again. Ms. C. said, "It was no different from any other event—we never talked about anything." The Polly Klass kidnapping/murder brought back this memory in terrifying detail, which she relived for weeks after Polly's body was found.

During early adolescence, two significant events changed her home environment. First, her brother left, and she recalled thinking, "Now I'm alone with them," with a sense of bleakness and isolation. The second was her father's leaving again. She recalled that they had little money, and she believed her mother had a nervous breakdown, because "she just stayed in her room and screamed at me."

Ms. C. described herself as having always liked school. She was popular with her teachers and peers, participated in activities, and got good grades. The wall in her room was covered with award certificates. However, her parents never seemed to notice anything she did. Rather, they always expected her to be totally self-reliant, from her earliest years in day care until the day she left home for college.

At age 12, she had her first sexual intercourse. She accompanied her parents to a party at the home of a couple with whom they were friends. Ms. C. was allowed to drink wine, and drank enough to feel drunk. The host then took her for a walk, during which she performed fellatio on him. When I asked her about her lack of affect in telling this story, she responded, "It was like telling a story about someone else. Like I was there, but I was not a participant." She described this event as a "turning point," although noting that somehow it was just a symptom of problems she was already having. After this, at age 13, she became a "party girl," drinking, smoking marijuana, and having sex with boyfriends—although no one boy stayed for very long.

For most of her childhood and adolescence, she experienced a sharp dichotomy between what she called her school/work "conservative girl" self and her party "rebel girl" self. She also referred to herself as "Teflon girl," which seemed to be her sense of detachment, or "never crying," and depersonalization, or "feeling like things were happening to someone else."

In high school, her public conservative girl self increasingly diverged from her private rebel girl self, and her cover of popularity and social acceptance finally fell apart in the 10th grade when she had sex with her best friend's boyfriend. Her friend became enraged, and spray-painted the words "whore" and "slut" on Ms. C.'s house, on the street in front of the house, on both family cars, and on Ms. C.'s locker at school. In addition, the now ex-friend carried on a campaign at school to turn Ms. C.'s peers against her. Ms. C.'s fall from grace was swift and total, and she decided to complete her 11th and 12th grades at a private high school within driving distance of her home.

Ms. C. changed schools, but not her behavior. She joined the "bad crowd" that smoked, drank, and partied. She had "lots of friends, but all the wrong kind." Her sexual acting out increased, now with no pretense of a relationship. She wrecked the family car by driving into a tree when she was drunk. During this time, she received two DUIs. Her parents threatened to institutionalize her, and she was put on juvenile probation with a court order to receive psychotherapy. She recalled that her therapist blamed her parents for her problems, which she liked, and that he seemed to be attracted to her. She recalled: "We laughed about my getting drunk and sleeping with lots of men, so I didn't think it was a problem."

In spite of her difficulties, Ms. C. managed to set good-enough grades in high school to qualify for admission to a high-status university. She recalled that the day her parents drove her to college, they dropped her off in front of the dorm with her suitcase and a bag of fruit and drove away. She briefly felt "at a total loss," then told herself, "You have to take care of yourself. Go upstairs and unpack and you'll be fine." Ms. C. continued, "There has always been this need for me to take care of myself. You're just plopped there, so deal with it. It makes me very independent."

The pattern that developed in early adolescence continued in college. She kept her grades up, but drank heavily, smoked marijuana, used cocaine, slept with "lots of guys," and graduated with honors. She completed an M.A. degree in her field, and decided not to pursue a Ph.D. degree after a professor she feared discouraged her from going on. Meanwhile, now established in her career, her lifestyle was still one of drinking, using illegal drugs, and sexually acting out. Wherever she went, her academic or professional "conservative girl" was extremely successful, while her recreational "rebel girl" continued the self-destructive behavior about which she later felt terrible. After her last boyfriend left her, her defenses were no longer successful in warding off her frightening depression, and she entered therapy to try to get help.

Differential Diagnosis: Major Categories

Ms. C.'s initial presentation was that of a clear, coherent, well-organized young woman. The only firm conclusion I could reach after the first session was that she showed no evidence of a thought disorder or severe depressive disorder. There is no doubt that she had been depressed for years, and, in fact, appeared to have had a mild major depressive episode when she and her boyfriend separated six months before she began therapy with me. However, her personal and family histories and her behavior during treatment supported the hypothesis that her depression rose out of the early and lasting deprivation characteristic of individuals with a disorder of the self.

It seemed fairly clear early on that Ms. C. did not possess the whole self- and object-representations characteristic of a neurotic disorder. As her therapy progressed, she revealed deep and opposing splits between her good and bad self- and object-representations. Her names for the self-parts are rebel girl, conservative girl, and Teflon girl. She described her internal experience of her object-parts as "reading the laundry list" (of self-vilifying accusations), judging her, telling her how fortunate she was or to quit feeling sorry for herself and go out and do something nice for others.

In addition, her defenses were not characteristic of a neurosis. The preoedipal defense of splitting rather than repression was evident early in the therapy. In addition, denial, avoidance, acting out (with drugs, alcohol, and sex), distancing, projection, and detachment characterized her behavior with me and in the world. Moreover, as became evident later in her work, she probably also had a dissociative disorder.

I saw little evidence of narcissistic grandiosity or mirroring or idealizing defenses in the initial hours of therapy, nor did I hear evidence of them in her history. Therefore, I tentatively ruled out the diagnosis of narcissistic disorder of the self.

The differential diagnosis between distancing borderline and schizoid disorders proved more difficult. The borderline has a split self- and object-representation characterized by a clinging self-part that feels "good" or rewarded for regressive behavior and a distancing self-part that feels "bad" (the affects of the abandonment depression) for real self-activation. In developmental terms, this unit is the RORU—the rewarding object relations unit within which the negotiated contract is to receive affirmation, acknowledgment, and approval for clinging and compliance rather than self-activating. The underlying unit is the WORU—the withdrawing object relations unit, within which the self-part is attacked and abandoned for activation.

Patients with a borderline disorder may externalize either the withdrawing part-unit or the rewarding part-unit. When the withdrawing object part-unit is externalized (the distancing borderline disorder), the patient projects the functions of judgment, hostile criticism, and abuse onto someone in the environment, and behaves in such ways as to minimize the expected/experienced damage. In other words, the patient is saying, "I feel bad, and you are causing it by your judgment, criticism, and hostility. If I can avoid, block, or control your hostility, I won't feel bad." This patient will intellectualize, detach, distance, act out, and use avoidance and denial to block anything that interferes with this defense. The affects of the rewarding unit (feeling good) may seem to be absent, but are safely contained internally, and are expressed in fantasy and reverie.

When the withdrawing object part-unit remains internalized (the clinging borderline disorder), the patient will experience the affects of the abandonment depression as arising internally, and defend against them by projecting the rewarding object-part onto the external object, and then cling or comply to get the object to "make it stop." In other words, the patient is saying, "I know you will love and take care of me if I don't self-activate. I'll please you by clinging and complying with your wishes, so you will take care of me, and these bad (abandonment) feelings will go away." This patient denies separateness from the object, and acts out "reunion fantasies" through clinging and compliance with avoidance of self-activation in order to keep the affects of the abandonment (separation) depression at bay.

Finally, patients with a borderline disorder often exhibit "some form of sadomasochistic sexual adaptation" owing to a continuation of parental scapegoating through the oedipal period.[5.2]

Patients with a schizoid disorder of the self have a very different internal dynamic. The defensive unit for the schizoid disorder is the master–slave unit, while the underlying unit is the sadist–self-in-exile unit. In contrast, borderline and narcissistic patients as children believe that there is a path to a relationship with the parents if they can find it, whereas schizoid patients, as children, feel that there is no path to a relationship with parents. The schizoid individual who moves toward connection will expect to be appropriated, exploited, dominated, coerced, and manipulated. The schizoid patient will accept some degree of this master-slave relatedness as a condition for achieving some connection with the therapist, and thereby with the world.

However, when the connection is experienced as being too appropriating, too manipulative, and coercive, "the fragile thread of connection may be broken, because the price of attachment has become too high." At this point, the projection of the sadistic object takes over, and the patient will withdraw into exile, which will be experienced as freedom. The schizoid individual probably will have a highly developed capacity for self-sufficiency, for the ability to operate alone, independently and autonomously. In fact:

> "The conscious awareness of this capacity for self-regulation, self-containment, and self-sufficiency is often highly developed early in the life of a schizoid. There is a kind of adultomorphism that goes on with the schizoid (child). . . . This premature taking of adult capacities and responsibilities often dramatically distinguishes the schizoid from other self disorders."

Differential Diagnosis Refined

Ms. C. presented a puzzling picture as I attempted to sort out whether she presented a borderline disorder of the self or a secret schizoid disorder. Diagnosis is essential, because for each diagnosis, the treatment interventions, aspects of the frame, pace and course of treatment, and even outcome goals can be different. Therefore, there is some urgency in arriving at a correct diagnosis as soon as possible after treatment begins. On the other hand, one of the main sources of information for the diagnosis is the patient's behavior in treatment, including responses to interventions, transference acting out, and responses to the frame. Therefore, the therapist must be prepared to reevaluate the diagnosis with every intervention, while staying the course with a diagnosis until sufficient evidence has accumulated to warrant a change.

Most diagnostic criteria apply to more than one category, and are distinctive only by their function for the patient and their placement (salience and intensity) in the unique configuration of diagnostic criteria. The criteria I shall examine in this case are transference acting out, self-activation, attachment style, reaction to separation, responses to interventions, and countertransference acting out.

Transference Acting Out

Patients with disorders of the self primarily enter therapy projecting one or another of their part-object representations onto the therapist. In most cases, it will be the so-called defensive unit, part-object. Masterson calls this nearly seamless projection "transference acting out" to distinguish it from "transference," in which a patient knows he or she is displacing feelings onto the therapist, because he or she is able to recognize the independent existence of the therapist. This patient may regress under stress to transference acting out, but typically will be able to maintain a therapeutic alliance, because he or she has the capacity to engage in whole self and object relations. Patients with a disorder of the self are largely unable to function at this level.

Ms. C. presented a picture of a competent, socially engaging, successful young woman. It was quickly evident that this was a false-self façade that had served to help her garner academic and occupational successes, but had also served to mask her painful internal struggles—and leave her to deal with them alone. However, initially I, too, was captivated by her polish and engaging manner, and in my countertransference, failed to address a severe problem that could have compromised any lasting effect of her therapy had it not been recognized and corrected. This will be addressed in the section on countertransference acting out.

Ms. C.'s reasons for resuming therapy after a six-month interval did not shed much light on this differential. At the outset, it was impossible to determine whether she was experiencing the secret schizoid's master–slave unit and moving toward the relatively safe attachment afforded by a relationship with a therapist, or the borderline rewarding self-part-unit, and moving toward a clinging relationship with a therapist because of the temporary lack of a relationship in her personal life.

Ms. C. adapted quickly to the frame of therapy. After the first session, she noted approvingly that I seemed to "mean business," and was not "flaky" like her previous therapist. When I asked her what "flaky" meant, she said that on one occasion her therapist had tried to hug her when she was crying, and she thought that was "strange—flaky." Theoretically, the borderline patient who clings would move toward the therapist's offering hugs as "rewards for regression." In this case, Ms. C. seemed to find it aversive—more like the distancing borderline or schizoid patient's fear of intrusion or appropriation.

Similarly, she adapted easily to the boundaries of the therapeutic frame. She arrived exactly on time, paid on time, never asked about phone calls, or made any other special requests. Again, the boundaries of the frame are thought to be an anathema to the clinging borderline patient. They engender feelings of separation and abandonment by the therapist, and are likely to evoke clinging or withdrawal. However, the distancing borderline patient would be more likely to see them as acceptable conditions of the withdrawing part-object, if other conditions did not become too intolerable. The intensity of the projection of the withdrawing part-object is carefully titrated by the distancing borderline patient in order to sustain receiving at least some rewarding part-object supplies, and the full magnitude of the withdrawing part-object projection may remain hidden for months. I believe that therapists often act out countertransference with these patients to avoid receiving this full projection, and in doing so collude with the patient's pull to resonate and "step into" the rewarding part-object. This collusion allows these patients to continue their self-destructive, acting-out behavior, which by definition negates anything else happening in therapy. As Freud first observed, patients act out to avoid remembering. It is a massive defense of the borderline patient, and until it is brought under control, therapy comes to a halt.

For the schizoid patient, the frame is more likely to minimize distortions arising from projection of the master onto the therapist. Safety is a critical condition of therapy for the schizoid patient, and the neutrality of the therapist and the frame of therapy establish a safe, trustworthy environment. This permits the schizoid patient to know where the therapist stands, and to feel that expectations are stable, predictable, and reasonable, and not arbitrary. Ms. C.'s ready adaptation to the frame appears to support a diagnosis of either a distancing borderline or a schizoid disorder.

Regarding her demeanor as a source of information, Ms. C. often spoke in the passive voice. In addition, her phrasing and the content of her material had an elusive circumscribed quality. I believed this denial of authorship was a distancing phenomenon and an important diagnostic clue, but in the beginning stages of therapy, I could not assign it conclusively to either the schizoid or the distancing borderline disorder.

Self-activation or Self-reliance

In my few sessions with Ms. C., I saw no consistent signs of clinging or difficulties in self-activation central to a diagnosis of a clinging borderline disorder. On the contrary, Ms. C. seemed to be able to activate herself effectively at work and in some areas of her personal life. She appeared to be the epitome of a self-reliant, successful businessperson. For example, within the first few weeks of beginning therapy, she successfully negotiated a dissolution of a partnership with a coworker that had been disadvantageous for her, hired and trained a new assistant, and traveled to several major cities in the United States to secure new accounts for her firm.

However, as therapy progressed, it became clear that I had not understood the function of the false-self presentation of Ms. C.'s conservative girl. I did not distinguish whether this conservative girl was the compensatory "I don't need anyone" expression of the self-reliant schizoid patient, or the "I'll look independent for you because it keeps you from criticizing me" of the distancing borderline patient. This issue was somewhat clarified by reaching a better understanding of Ms. C.'s attachment style.

Attachment Style

Ms. C.'s relationships with both men and women seemed to be characterized by her moves toward connection with others, followed by a rapid retreat. This behavior initially appeared to be more characteristic of the schizoid disorder. However, the picture is more complicated when the function of her behavior is considered.

For the clinging borderline disorder, the movement toward the object should be accompanied by projection of the rewarding internal object-representation onto the external object, cessation of self-activation, and clinging to this external object in order to feel good. (Keep in mind that "feeling good" for these patients may mean nothing more than escaping from the abandonment depression. They may actually feel terrible—hung over, sick, downtrodden—but experience profound internal, unconscious "reinforcement" for their defensive behavior because they have escaped from the abandonment depression.)

The distancing borderline disorder should be accompanied by projection of the withdrawing object relations unit onto the external object (the therapist), experiencing this object as critical and judgmental, and escaping from this object in order to "feel good." Ms. C. did not appear to fit this pattern. However, in arriving at this conclusion, I had misperceived the distancing, intellectualizing, detached functions of her conservative girl in forestalling the (projected) criticism of the object. Instead, I believed Ms. C. was exhibiting the behavior of the schizoid dilemma.

Moving toward and away from the object has a very different function for the schizoid patient than it does for the distancing borderline patient. As noted above, the clinging borderline patient internalizes the withdrawing part-object, and projects the rewarding object in order to receive supplies and avoid experiencing affects of the abandonment depression. The distancing borderline patient, on the other hand, projects the withdrawing part-object, and distances to escape from these affects. The schizoid disordered patient moves toward the object for supplies, but expects to be controlled, appropriated, and exploited in return. When the patient believes these events have happened beyond a tolerable limit, she must flee into exile to escape total appropriation. In addition, Masterson and Klein observe that while many schizoid individuals present with obvious withdrawalness, there are many fundamentally schizoid people who present with an engaging, interactive personality style. The category is designated the "secret schizoid."

Ms. C.'s history of interpersonal relations appeared to be more characteristic of the secret schizoid disorder. During the first few weeks of therapy, she reported initiating contacts with several new men, dating them (usually involving having sex on the first or second date), finding them all unsatisfactory for one reason or another, and moving on to others within the space of a few days. This pattern, in combination with the report of her emotionally abusive 18-month relationship with her boyfriend, in which she described herself as "completely giving up myself," living in prison, and being tortured, completely controlled, and treated sadistically, gave further weight to the diagnosis of schizoid. It appeared that Ms. C. moved toward these relationships in the master–slave unit. Once she enters a relationship, she "gets hooked" and experiences herself as a slave—totally appropriated by her master partner. And indeed, the men she selects often do seem to be inappropriate in these ways. Later in her treatment, she was able to acknowledge that she was not drawn to men who treated her well. Only those who had an edge of danger or intrigue (sadism?), and who treated her with indifference, seemed to "hook her" and arouse her sexually. Once hooked, she lost herself, and tolerated abusive treatment until, in Masterson and Klein's words, "a certain critical line has been crossed." At this time, "the projection of the sadistic object is experienced, and the self has no choice but to retreat." Finally, even after she "escaped" from her abusive boyfriend, she believed she was still vulnerable to being recaptivated by him. She discussed him with anger and fear, feelings of attraction and aversion.

At this point, it should be noted that whereas depression and rage lie at the center of all abandonment depressions, the schizoid will also experience intolerable anxiety, alienation, isolation, longing, devaluation, deprivation, and danger. When Ms. C. experienced the termination of her 18-month relationship, she felt all of these affects with frightening intensity. She vowed to "never allow herself to become that involved with anyone again," and then later sadly acknowledged that it was probably inevitable that she would.

However, as therapy progressed and the functions of Ms. C.'s part-units became clearer, it seemed that the conservative girl was activated to control (receiving supplies) and then distance from others, who were quickly experienced as being too judgmental and critical. In this role, Ms. C. was primarily interested in keeping others from finding out the truth about her "laundry list" of misdeeds and characteristics, of which she was deeply ashamed, rather than maintaining a safe distance from exploitation and indifference. Similarly, her rebel girl appeared to have the function of moving toward attachment and feeling good by being "fun, cute, popular, and paying attention to others so they will like me," rather than an expression of the controlled and dominated slave of the schizoid "attachment-seeking" unit. In other words, "If you're not needed, you're just an afterthought. If I don't act peppy and fun to be around, they won't want me." About nine months into therapy, Ms. C. described the feelings she was having about a man she had dated a few times, and her experience of clinging and resistance to self-activation emerged more clearly.

> "I want to succumb to the feeling. I'm restraining myself from falling into it. It's a terrible crevasse to fall into. I get obsessive, and I'm on the edge of it. I have to stop myself. It almost seems like an overwhelming feeling to me. I want to talk to him all the time. Call him 100 times a day. I feel like I'm going to lose myself—I'm barely in control. I can't have an opinion, say what I want to, do anything on my terms. I worship the person. Men say they like women who agree with them, but really they ultimately like a woman who has her own mind, so I lose them. I just want to say, 'Please don't leave me.' The only thing that is important to me is being with them. I feel like a 12-year-old. I want to be married, but I don't have the emotional maturity. . . . I want to be completely taken care of. It's

a daily effort to keep life going. I'm exhausted. I have to stand up for myself, and I don't want to do it. It's almost like I'd like to be an observer. . . . I just want this vision of crying in bed and having someone hold me. But at the moment I wanted to be together, he'd totally deny me. I'd beg him to come back."

Reaction to Separation

Ms. C. reported that early separations from her parents, such as childhood trips to California to visit grandparents, or running away from home after graduating from high school to live with a man, were experienced as a wonderful relief, an escape. When her parents dropped her off in front of the dorm on the day she entered college, she briefly felt at a total loss, then told herself, "You have to take care of yourself. Go upstairs and unpack and you'll be fine." There's always been this need for me to take care of myself. You're just plopped there, so deal with it. It makes me very independent."

Another piece of information about her ability to separate arose when she changed her residence shortly after beginning therapy with me. She decided to move to a city nearer her work, gave notice to her roommates, found a new roommate, and moved—all within a few weeks and with a minimum of emotional disruption. Once again, this seeming ability to be self-reliant and to tolerate separation (given the other defenses noted above) seems much more characteristic of the schizoid than of the borderline disorder.

The real meaning of these events, however, did not emerge until much later in therapy. For example, regarding her experience of being dropped off in front of the dorm, Ms. C. later observed that people reject her (like that) because she's "not worthy of being treated better." Similarly, regarding her changing apartments and so roommates, she later observed, "They were probably glad to see me go. I think they didn't like me." Here the projection of the withdrawing unit object-part becomes increasingly clear, and the experience of self-reliant escape to freedom of the schizoid disorder is totally absent.

Responses to Interventions

When I began to consistently use interventions couched to point out what I believed was Ms. C.'s schizoid dilemma regarding regulating feelings of safety by moving toward and away from others, she appeared to settle into therapy and started to reveal more about herself. However, her revelations often brought contradictory information, and were usually devoid of appropriate affect. For example, she frequently reported that yet another relationship was on the rocks. I would note that moving toward any chance of a real relationship seemed to be so dangerous to her that she created conditions for its failure, but when it failed, she was once again alone and lonely. She would sigh, acknowledge that this was true, and talk more revealingly about her experiences. But as she talked, she would sound less and less as though she were responding to fear of appropriation, exploitation, control, and indifference, and more as though she were experiencing the rapid oscillation of the rewarding and withdrawing units of the distancing borderline disorder. For example, she would move toward a relationship; engage in a kind of ritualized, sexual acting out; relinquish her self; and then the relationship would end, accompanied by Ms. C.'s projecting the critical hostile object-part or the depleted self-part onto the boyfriend.

> "When guys don't call back, I can make it be either I'm too smart, too independent, or too successful, or that I'm not pretty, too serious—whatever qualities I have, they're not good. If he sleeps with me, I feel 'OK, he likes me.' Then when I don't hear from him, I think he's used me. So he doesn't call, well, I prepare myself for that, so when it happens, I try not to have a bad feeling. I put up a barrier on date number three. If a guy reveals something personal, I have no inclination to do that. I'll just be rejected so I can't risk it. I don't trust them. They'll walk on you. People will take advantage of you. I'm not emotionally revealing to them."

It was becoming increasingly clear that Ms. C. did not leave a relationship to escape from domination, control, and exploitation as one would expect from a schizoid experience. She believes she was left—rejected—because she was unworthy, and then feels used and taken advantage of. To compensate, she can reassure herself that she is really superior to the boyfriend, but this devaluation is a weak rationalization covering the louder, insistent internal voice that tells her of her inadequacies that caused the boyfriend to leave her.

As treatment progressed, other separations appeared to have been accomplished without a backward glance. I now began to see them from a different perspective. Ms. C. would report a cavalier indifference to "what people think," and would later observe that she conducted her behavior almost exclusively with the hope of getting what she called "reinforcement."

In response to my interpreting what I perceived to be her schizoid dilemma, Ms. C. revealed many incidents in her life that had caused her embarrassment, shame, and, in some cases, self-loathing. It was clear that she felt she could talk openly with me, and she affirmed my impression by saying that she felt she trusted me—that I would not judge her. This also made me question my diagnosis. I wondered whether she was too trusting too quickly for a schizoid disorder, and too concerned with judgment rather than with being exploited or controlled. However, during the first few months of therapy, she was experiencing affect when she revealed these incidents, and seemed increasingly engrossed in her therapy, so I put away my misgivings.

Ms. C. continued to reveal aspects of her sexual exploits, many of which she said she had never discussed with anyone before. She repeated that she had felt like a bad girl as long as she could remember, starting with getting in trouble for writing pages and pages of "dirty words" as a first-grader, to getting drunk and picking up men in hotel bars as a teenager, to dancing in a strip bar contest, going to bars in "dangerous parts of town," being picked up and going with men to their apartments for drugs and sex, and the like. Ms. C. stated that on at least several such occasions, she felt as though she were someone else, and seemed to be doing these things "on automatic."

At one point later in therapy while talking about her father's absence from the family and her mother's "nervous breakdown," Ms. C. exclaimed that she hoped she wasn't going to find out that she had been molested by her father. After that one comment, she was reluctant to explore this topic, although she did once allude to a concern that "something might have happened." In retrospect, I believe that her emotional detachment, her sense of having been a "bad girl" and depressed all her life, the paucity of memory about her relationship with her father, and later experiences of "going on automatic" and easily approaching men for sex from the age of 12 or 13, support the hypothesis that she might have been molested. However, she also appears to have been traumatized by her early experience of being taken into the woods by a strange man when she was 7 years old. I believe she has a posttraumatic stress disorder with dissociative defenses, but not enough information is available to confirm this diagnosis. Nevertheless, when PTSD with dissociative defenses coexists with a disorder of the self, treatment is first directed to the personality disorder.

As her treatment progressed, her experience of relationships became increasingly clear. For example, while she described herself as being under the control of her boyfriend during their 18-month relationship, she later acknowledged that she just wanted him to take over her life for her—to make all the decisions. Later, after another quick-sex relationship failed, she admitted:

> "I feel I'm a very sexual person. But there are two sides. I like it, and think that it's OK. But I think I use that. If I'm with a guy I think I'm not good enough for, then I try to snag him by sleeping with him. I don't feel confident, so I try to mold myself into what I think they're going to like. I feel like a fake in that he doesn't know I've slept around. I don't trust them to tell me. . . . I just want somebody to take care of me. I don't want the responsibility of running my life. Being independent wears on me, even though sometimes I'm real proud of me. When a guy leaves me, he takes part of me with him. In the initial stages [of dating], I do better. I kind of control things. But when I get attached, I get kind of weird. I, like, lose myself. I identify with what I think they were looking for and try to make myself into that person. . . . I have done so many bad things. I've slept with all those people, and I drink too much. I've done drugs, gone out with married men. I feel like a horrible person."

And when she feels like a horrible person, she projects the judgmental, critical object, then withdraws, and reverts to acting out the conservative girl. I was beginning to get the picture with increasing clarity, and to feel that unless I confronted Ms. C. about the self-destructive consequences of her acting out with sex, illegal drugs, and alcohol abuse—set the reality frame—her therapy would not progress.

Countertransference Acting Out

I was forced to look at the fact that although Ms. C. was disclosing information she had never talked about before with appropriate affect, her extremely self-destructive acting-out behavior continued undiminished. Nor did she see the contradiction in her own statements that, on the one hand, sex was fine, and, on the other, that she felt like a horrible person because of her sexual acting out.

Several months into therapy, I finally woke up to the realization that I had not effectively confronted her about her behavior. In retrospect, I believe I was captivated by her conservative girl. In addition, if she was exhibiting the conservative girl, I was receiving the projection of the withdrawing part-object, and I'm sure I wanted to contain it and avoid fully bringing this negative projection into the open. So, like her previous therapists, I remained in collusion with her rewarding part-object, and by so doing, I failed to bring her face to face with the destructive aspects of her behavior. In addition, I believe my understanding of her attachment style, her defenses, and her intrapsychic structure that led to my diagnosis of a schizoid disorder was another way of avoiding dealing with this projection.

Distancing Borderline Disorder: Confrontation of Acting-Out Defenses

When I began confronting her by calling attention to the destructiveness of her sexual acting out, it produced the exact opposite and left her feeling terrible about herself. She quickly rationalized that she needed attention, was frightened of being depressed if she did not get feedback, and that besides, she liked sex, and wondered what was wrong with that. I continued to focus on her rationalization and denial of the destructiveness of her behavior, noting that when she got drunk and slept with a man whom she barely knew, she felt terrible about herself. If she felt lonely and depressed about not having a date, at least there was a purpose to it. I noted, "When you avoid these feelings of loneliness and sadness by drinking and sleeping around, you really feel terrible. That doesn't add up."

A turning point was reached when Ms. C. proudly announced she had placed an advertisement in the personals column of a local newspaper to meet some men. I called to her attention her experiences in the past of picking up men, getting drunk, doing drugs, and sleeping with the men as a quick fix to feel better, after which she really felt terrible about herself, and that she was setting herself up for repeating this cycle in spades. At this point, she got angry, began pouting and accusing me of judging and criticizing her and trying to stop her from enjoying life, and threatened to quit therapy.

The projection of the withdrawing object-part-unit had broken out into the open, and I could now address it directly. I asked her why, when I called to her attention the destructiveness of her behavior, which she described to me with deep shame and regret in the previous session, she felt I was criticizing her. She continued with her angry, pouting, adolescent-like behavior and accusations. I replied that she was using these accusations to ignore what I said so that she wouldn't have to look directly at it. I pointed out that when she used the word "enjoy" to describe behavior that she knew was self-destructive, made her feel terrible about herself, and made it impossible for her to reach her goal of having a family, she was really denying her own knowledge of how self-destructive her behavior had been for years.

Ms. C. slowly began to bring her acting out under control. She stopped drinking, and observed that when she did not drink excessively, she was less likely to feel she had to have sex to make men like her.

As she was beginning to bring her acting out under control, she was also reexamining her relationship with her parents and revisiting her understanding of historical material with more appropriate affects of sadness and anger—Teflon girl was shedding her lining.

She had begun to be open to confrontation about her defensive false-self presentation. During one session several months after I began steady confrontation, she despaired about her loneliness, noting that she sat at home on the couch wondering whom to call, or just sat there staring into space, waiting for someone to call her. She turned to me and said, "So, when I'm lonely, what should I do?"

I replied that she was now aware that the things she had done to get away from these feelings had not worked. In fact, they are dangerous and make her feel worse about herself, so why would she continue? I pointed out that conservative girl, rebel girl, and Teflon girl are all ways to get away from her real feelings. These "girls" provide quick fixes, but ultimately they have the opposite effect. Now she is faced with not using these escapes, and developing a way to face her real feelings instead of doing self-destructive things to get away from them. Not doing so has kept her from having the very things most important to her in her life—a home and a family of her own. She was silent for a long while, finally responding in a sad voice, "I guess I feel like I'm left to my own devices now, and it immobilizes me. But there's no one I can call about that, is there?"

Ms. C. is still in treatment. She is diagnosed as a distancing borderline disorder of the self with possible PTSD. She has contained her acting out and has begun to see some benefit to her hard work. She has been dating a man who appears to be interested in having a real relationship, and has been able to contain her sexual acting out and her "slide" into losing herself. However, her hold on relinquishing these lifelong defenses is precarious, and I suspect she may have many more rounds to go before she is able to feel confident enough to face the affects of the abandonment depression.

CASE 2:

SCHIZOID, NARCISSISTIC, OR BORDERLINE DISORDER?*

Identifying Information

Ms. R., a 38-year-old married woman who lives with her husband, holds a mid-management position in a large corporation. She, by choice, has no children. She is a short, noticeably quiet and reserved woman—clearly intelligent and extremely articulate.

Presenting Problem

In January 1995, Ms. R. presented to a large HMO Psychiatry Department, complaining of depression. She stated, "I've not felt good

*Case courtesy of Margot T. Beattie, Ph.D.

lately; the world has lost its luster." She also complained of chronic headaches and low libido.

History of Presenting Problem

Ms. R. dates the onset of her depression to several years earlier following a robbery at her home. She was tearful as she related this episode. She didn't seek either medical or psychiatric help at the time of this incident; her husband was out of town. She waited two years to get help because "life was tolerable." Her sleep had been poor for a long time—even preceding the robbery. Her appetite was normal. She had taken an antidepressant prescribed by her internist for four weeks and noticed no improvement. She had subjective complaints of depressed mood, difficulty concentrating at work, loss of libido, and ruminating thoughts of hurt, anger, death, and loss. She disclaimed being suicidal and has no history of suicide attempts. She is not dependent on alcohol or drugs. Ms. R. has a family history of depression. A younger sister had been treated medically for depression and once was suicidal. She believes that both of her parents were depressed, saying that her deceased mother wrote of these feelings in her diary, and she reports that her father is currently depressed.

Family History

Ms. R. is the oldest of three children with one sister, 36, and a brother, 32. She was born and raised in a religious Christian family in the Midwest. She was never physically abused or sexually molested. She said of her family, "My family was loving, but not expressive—we never talked to each other much." Her father is an architect in her hometown. Her mother died of colon cancer 14 years earlier when Ms. R. was 24 years old.

Parental History

Ms. R. comes from talented and intellectual parents. Her mother was gifted musically and Ms. R. learned to play several musical instruments. She described her mother as "the center of the family." She was raised in a religious tradition that taught that everything good and right comes from God and that everything difficult is "unreal and of the mortal mind." Ms. R. recalled that it was not OK to "feel bad" and sees this familial belief as part of her self-demand for perfection. Ms. R. said, "Mother and I did things together, but neither of us was the talkative type. She loved to garden and I'd pull weeds beside her. She loved botany and our hikes became wildflower-collecting expeditions." Ms. R.'s father had many diverse interests and abilities. Ms. R. said, "Everything came to him almost magically." When he became interested in something, he would research it, become skilled in it, and form organizations to share his interest and expertise with others. These interests included sports, artistic endeavors, and history.

Ms. R.'s Role in the Family

As the eldest child, Ms. R. was expected to be responsible. When asked about her childhood, she looked perplexed and said in all seriousness, "I never was a child." She described her upbringing as "absolute." She learned to cook, clean, and shop for food with her mother. "It seems that I always knew how to cook—I don't remember learning to cook." When asked how this was for her, she responded, "It didn't feel like a burden; it was just the way things were." Ms. R. seemed to be a bystander in her family.

In spite of so many family interests, Ms. R. was not actively included. She took part in some of her father's interests, but said, "Mostly I just watched him; sometimes there was a quiet companionship." She described doing things, when instructed, without much personal participation. Once, on a fishing trip, she carefully followed instructions and succeeded in casting her line and catching a fish. She said, "There was no feeling of defeat or triumph. I just did it. So much of my life was doing without involvement. I used to go along with them to some of their [her parents'] dance activities, but in a form of detachment—I still live that way. Once I thought the detachment was due to the religious teaching that the material world was nonreal—now I'm not so sure."

As a child, she said, she imagined a man explaining her to others—an intermediary. She continued, "It was an imaginary audience. He was not praising me; he was justifying me, like saying, 'See, she knows what she's doing even if it doesn't show.' " This pronounced observing of herself through seemingly separate eyes is still present. She referred to this part of herself as "the watcher."

School Years

Ms. R. was always a good student. As a teenager, she worked in her father's office. When she went to college, she planned to major in English, but said, "I had no vision or goal and others were better, so I dropped out to work (after her junior year)." She learned at an early age to take care of herself; following an auto accident, for example, she went to a friend's house to cry and clean up before going home. At 20, she undertook what she described as a "delayed adolescent rebellion" and moved out of the family home into an apartment where she could smoke cigarettes and stay up all night.

Adulthood

At 22, Ms. R. married a man whom she met in college. She divorced him two years later. She said that she had never loved him, but had married him out of "passive acquiescence": "He had a plan and I didn't." She went on, "The day before the wedding, I had a sense of doom. My father noticed it and asked, 'You OK?' I said 'Yes.' I didn't say No because I didn't have a reason." One of Ms. R.'s deepest sorrows is that her mother didn't live to see her outgrow her counterculture phase. "She never saw the person I became; she would have been proud."

Ms. R. went back to her hometown when her father informed her of the seriousness of her mother's health. Her description of her mother's illness was wrenching. "It was dreadful. I didn't know what to do, I didn't know how to comfort her, support her, or help her in any way. I tried to make her soup and it was too salty. We never spoke of her dying and my father never said anything. All that denial was no help."

When she was notified by her father that her mother had died, she again returned to her hometown to scatter her mother's ashes. In describing how she dealt with her mother's death, she said, "I came back to California and went back to everything as usual; back to work with a quiet numbness. I knew she was dying and blamed myself that I didn't do anything for her—a lot of recrimination. I didn't have the intimacy to talk about it with anyone—I kept it all inside—it solidified over the years. Usually I try to stifle it: Does anyone really cry without feeling self-conscious? The watcher says, 'This is enough.' I suppose I have always grieved for her, but not to the point of healing."

Following her divorce, she entered a year of psychotherapy, became more independent, and "claimed California for her home." She met friends through an organization she joined and moved into her own apartment. She initially worked in clerical jobs, but was quickly tapped for promotions into management. In 1989, she married her current husband.

Differential Diagnosis

Axis I

Include diagnoses of major depression and rule out PTSD. Ms. R. had come into treatment on an antidepressant, and once referred for a medication evaluation, her medication was changed. She met the DSM-IV criteria for major depression with dysphoric mood, loss of interest and pleasure in almost all usual activities, sleep disturbance in the form of early-morning awakening, loss of energy, fatigue, and diminished ability to think and concentrate. She also described a traumatic event of being robbed that she identified as the precipitant of her depression.

In considering PTSD, although she had a numbed responsiveness to the external world and a feeling of detachment or estrangement from others, constricted affect, sleep disturbance, and difficulty concentrating, all DSM-IV criteria for the diagnosis of PTSD, she lacked any reexperiencing of the trauma in recollections, dreams, or feelings. From her history, it became clear that the robbery experience had probably strained fragile defenses that, prior to the event, enabled her to ignore the long-standing symptoms listed above—symptoms that, incidentally, describe the experience of a schizoid personality disorder. I therefore put the PTSD diagnosis on the shelf, and diagnosed her on Axis I—with major depression.

Axis II

From the beginning of treatment, the two leading clues to Ms. R.'s diagnosis of self disorder were (1) her pervasive focus on the object, and (2) her profound detachment of affect. Although all self disorders focus on the object, they do so for different reasons.

My first impression of Ms. R. was that she had a schizoid personality disorder. This impression was based on her presentation of herself as aloof, removed, and highly precise and was contained in her responses and interactions with me. As I worked with her and observed the slightly superior quality of her aloof demeanor, and the extraordinary degree of compliance in her behavior toward me, I began to wonder whether she might not have a closet narcissistic personality disorder. And then when I noticed that she did not idealize me or anyone else in her world, and has considerable difficulty with self-activation, I considered a diagnosis of distancing borderline.

Closet Narcissistic Considerations

Her predominant focus on the object with pervasive compliance; an obsessional, perfectionist style; and an aloof, removed, and mildly superior demeanor led me to consider a closet narcissistic disorder. In contrast with the exhibitionist narcissistic disorder, the closet narcissistic disorder places primary investment in the object rather than in the self-representation. Ms. R.'s attention is pervasively directed toward the object and she assumes a position of excessive compliance, adjusting her own behavior almost exclusively to the anticipated reaction of others. I wondered if her compliance might not be her effort to remain fused with an idealized object or to fend off anticipated criticism from the aggressive fused part-unit. However, over time she demonstrated no idealization of others to support omnipotent perceptions. She, in fact, shows no evidence of internal fusion in her representations of self with others. In contrast, she is decidedly separate in her perceptions of herself and others.

At the same time I was sorting out her experience of object-representations, I noticed, in keeping with closet narcissistic considerations, that she had a self-representation that fluctuated between a surface presentation of mild superiority to a more secretive deflated (or stymied) self-image. There was a sense of grandiosity in some of her descriptions of herself. She has a talent for creating poster advertisements for the conferences of an organization to which she belongs. In response to not winning a prize for her efforts, she stated:

> "None of the top entries get recognition. Mine had an elegant, opalescent, mysterious look, but the awards went to the blatant. It's a metaphor for how I feel in life. I do very well, but the world doesn't appreciate it. I like to create magnificence, there was a thrill to what I did. But my evil twin says, 'It would be nice to get some recognition.' I'm pissed and disappointed; I left unsatisfied."

While her words have the flavor of grandiosity, these are secret talents of hers and her reference to its being "evil" to want recognition for herself flies in the face of the sense of entitlement common in narcissistic disorders.

Developmentally, Ms. R. did not describe being a receptacle for parental idealizing projections; her parents were too busy being self-activated.

These findings are sufficient to rule out a closet narcissistic disorder, but to strengthen the case, she does not look to me for mirroring responses, nor does she respond to them as one would expect. When used by me to acknowledge her experience, she responds with a strained tolerance, as if it is tiresome when I do not add more to her understanding of herself. In retrospect, a mirroring response to schizoid patients feels like a usurpation and they, in response, retreat.

Borderline Considerations

As I moved from the closet narcissistic diagnosis, I briefly considered a diagnosis of distancing borderline. Her aloof and removed demeanor could be a distancing defense (transference acting out) to her projection of the withdrawing part-unit. However, she did not vacillate between rewarding and withdrawing projections. These projections are not present. I do feel a pressure from her for me to take the lead in session and initially thought this could be a manifestation of clinging—an avoidance of the triad of self-activation leading to depression, leading to defense. In hindsight, as I worked harder for clarity, I realize that her turning to me was not out of a sense of helplessness that is part of the borderline self-identity struggle, but was born of deference, caution, and precise social etiquette. Her stance appears primarily self-protective. She reminds me of a graceful bird that, with great caution, alights briefly and carefully to feed.

Developmentally, while she described a background of considerable emotional restriction, she did not describe parents who used her to regulate their own moods or who rewarded regression and punished autonomy. Quite the opposite, her parents were unique, autonomous, and capable individuals, and she was expected from an early age to be, like them, wholly self-sufficient.

Schizoid Personality Disorder

I suspect you have guessed from the beginning that Ms. R. suffers from a schizoid personality disorder. Home for the schizoid patient is usually in the nonattachment unit and Ms. R. lives primarily within the sadistic object/self-in-exile unit. She is wary of me because I represent to her a risk of sliding into the schizoid master–slave unit of attachment. These two units are clearly and painfully described by her. Listen carefully and you can hear voices of both the sadistic object/self-in-exile unit and the master–slave unit. She said:

> "I had a headache yesterday and didn't want to go to this party, but I went anyway for D. All I wanted to do was to be alone in the dark and the quiet. Even getting my shoes out of the closet felt good . . . a critical voice says, 'You know you are committed (to going), it's part of the plan, it doesn't work to disappoint people. He'll feel bad and then you'll feel bad.' I feel lost and feel, now what do I do? It doesn't work to back out . . . Coming home from the party, I wanted comfort. I need to be alone. With someone else I have to have my antenna up to monitor where we are going with this."

In response to her complaints of a mysterious grinding fatigue at her job and her alluding to carefully gauging her interactions with others, I interpreted the schizoid dilemma to her, saying, "It seems to me you try to be involved with your coworkers, but you find it frightening and exhausting, and you make yourself safe by moving away, by making distance from them. So there's a constant movement back and forth with your never being content in either place."

She responded:

> "It's a funny balance. Usually I'm happy to be alone, but sometimes I want people. The past few months I've been talking more at work and it's been rewarding—like talking as opposed to being alone in my office. Even with having good times with others though, I'm ecstatic the moment I'm alone in the bathroom stall. Like hotel bathrooms where the stalls go from floor to ceiling and you can shut the world out. I come out refreshed from time by myself. It's also a pretty space—I can sit on the couch there and take stock and feel pampered."

And, if you're still in doubt, she has, since childhood, engaged in what she calls her "womb game," probably a pathognomonic sign of schizoid disorder.

> "I always had difficulty with getting up and going to school. I would play a game of 'womb space' and I didn't want to come out. I was warm and separate from everyone else. Bed was warm and I was alone and resting, not on call to serve their needs. I love to be alone. I feel it so deeply. I feel it in my chest and just want to cry. I listen to others at parties just to be social and I'm putting up with their conversations, being attentive to others when I'm too exhausted to pay attention."

The schizoid patient is driven into relationships by need and out of relationships by fear. Ms. R. captured the schizoid's experience of "no place to rest" when she said:

> "My husband is out of town and I go home and overeat and watch TV. I thought, 'I'll be self-indulgent,' but I also feel at a loss. What do I want to do? Nothing. I drift through the night. I have the freedom from interaction that I crave, but I'm not happy on my own. There's a letdown of 'now I've got it, and it doesn't feel good.' It's ironic that people find me calming, but I can't provide it for myself."

Ms. R.'s main affects are futility and hopelessness. Fairbairn[5.1] considered the sense of "futility" to be the primary schizoid affect. The self-in-exile is not only a form of protection from the sadistic object, but a resigned existence, having lost the *desired* object, what Guntrip calls the "desired deserter." Developmentally, Ms. R. describes her relationship with her parents in terms consistent with Dr. Klein's description of "parallel play." She shared in activities with her mother and father, but with little personal interaction with them.

Ms. R.'s background is characterized by emotional neglect. But there is a positive element in this picture. As restricted as her religious training was, it also offered her a structure and a reason for her parents' emotional distance. It wasn't all because she was "bad." She suffers from a childhood in which detachment of affect was the goal and the norm. I like the phrase "ambient trauma" used by Dr. Edna Mordecai to describe those experiences that have not been integrated and cannot be expressed because they were not "events" about which a story can be encoded into language. Ambient trauma is the reason Ms. R. suffers so much and is mystified by the depths of her own unhappiness. The quality of her early relationships, together with a strict religious doctrine that denies the reality of illness and individual pain, promoted a life of extreme self-sufficiency. But fatigue and despair are the hidden companions of self-sufficiency.

Countertransference and Therapeutic Technique

I am careful in the presence of Ms. R.; I fear I might scare her away. I am somewhat guarded in my emotional response to her, as I think that my understanding of her may feel to her like she is being appropriated by me. I always look forward to our time to work together. I have used interpretations of her schizoid compromises (work stance is half in/half out, chronic headaches are a clever compromise) when I realize I need to spend more time with her mapping out the actual schizoid dilemma. She is responding well and the therapy has deepened to her revealing more about her mother's death and her dissatisfaction with her marriage. She is poised to bring her feelings into her awareness and into the room.

CASE 3:

CLOSET NARCISSISTIC DISORDER, BORDERLINE DISORDER, OR SCHIZOID DISORDER?*

Ms. A. is a petite brunette, 25-year-old, unmarried accounting student. She is bouncy and attractive and laughs easily, often at herself. At the time she entered therapy, she was working in a bank and was about to graduate from business school.

Chief Complaint

Ms. A. says that she often feels needy, alone, and afraid. She is very nervous about making the transition from being a graduate student working part-time to becoming an accountant. She feels intimidated whenever she thinks of the future and the decisions she will have to make for herself.

History of Present Illness

Ms. A. has to take a licensing exam in a few months and she knows that until then she needs to focus solely on studying. This means that her normal way of coping with stress—going to a bar, drinking, picking up a man and becoming totally absorbed in their relationship—will be unavailable to her if she takes her work seriously. The thought of being alone and coping with her feelings by herself while she studies makes her feel frightened and overwhelmingly needy. This feels especially acute to her now because, for the first time in her life, she is living by herself in her own apartment and trying not to distract herself with men. Ms. A. says that she entered therapy to get help with managing her feelings during this difficult time, because she is afraid that otherwise she will not stay focused on her goals.

*Case courtesy of Elinor Greenberg, Ph.D.

Ms. A. does not take drugs, but she does go through periods in which she drinks to excess to escape her feelings. She is not an alcoholic, but she knows that alcoholism is a severe family problem and could be dangerous for her.

Ms. A.'s father was physically abusive to her older brothers, but he did not hit her or her sisters. There was no history of sexual abuse.

Although anxious about this upcoming stress in her life, Ms. A. does not appear to be particularly depressed. She seems generally optimistic about her life and proud of what she has accomplished so far. For this reason, I ruled out an affective disorder.

Previous Psychiatric Illness and Treatment

Ms. A. first entered therapy to cope with feelings of depression and what she called her "shyness." She attended a small junior college near her home because she had been afraid to go to a large university where she did not know anyone. Ms. A. said that her therapy was extremely helpful in that it gave her a perspective on her family, taught her to think more positively, and made her realize that she tended to become overinvolved with people too quickly.

When she moved to New York to attend business school, she began to participate in Alanon meetings as a way to meet new people and to support herself emotionally. These meetings were not enough to sustain her functioning and she has continued to try to deal with her feelings of loneliness by drinking and having chaotic, tumultuous relationships with men.

Family History

The Mother

Ms. A. describes her mother, who is 67 years old, as someone who feels that she had done her job as a mother if the house is neat and her children are clean. She leaves all major decisions and how the children should be disciplined up to her drunken, abusive husband. Ms. A.'s mother is very religious and feels that an unmarried daughter should live at home under the supervision of her family.

The patient says that she has always felt as though her mother has not made up her mind as to whether Ms. A. is good or bad, is lovable or unlovable. She says that she has always wanted her mother to approve of her, but that her mother is cold and hard to please. When she was little, she reports that she enjoyed dressing up and going to church with her mother and helping her clean the house. She said she always felt that "my mom knows best" and that that idea gave her a sense of security. She would get approval from her mother by drinking with her. In her teens, she and her mother began to fight, and now, on the rare occasions that she goes home, she drinks to deal with her negative feelings about her mother.

The Father

Ms. A.'s 70-year-old father is a salesperson for a local company. Ms. A. describes him as controlling and unpredictable. When he is in a good mood, he can be generous and talkative. However, frequently he is morose, brooding, and abusive. When her older brother was in his early teens, her father would go after him with a belt because he felt insulted by what he considered the youth's "insolence." Ms. A. has been scared of her father for as long as she can remember.

Nevertheless, when she was 5 or 6 years of age, Ms. A. remembers looking up to her father and wanting to please him. She has some pleasant memories from that period of feeling like her father's confidante. She did not realize that her father was an alcoholic until she was in her teens. She says that although her father never hit her, she does remember being chased around the house by him when he was mad at her. She often heard her mother and her father arguing, but does not think that he hit her mother. When Ms. A.'s father was drunk and angry with her, he would call her names and tell her she would never amount to anything because she had a bad attitude.

Ms. A. has always wanted her father's approval. She says that without it, she has difficulty feeling good about herself. Basically, she tried to please her father by getting good grades, acting the part of the good daughter, and in general trying to do everything "his way" when she was around him.

During Ms. A.'s teenage years, she began actively to avoid her father whenever she could. They stopped speaking almost entirely and she started to do things of which her father disapproved behind his back.

Her decision to leave home to pursue a career was the first time she openly acted against his wishes.

Outside of the home, her father acted very differently and was generally perceived as nice, helpful, and generous to others.

There were no other significant caretakers.

The Siblings

The patient is the youngest of four children. Next is a brother who is 2 years older, then a brother who is 4 years older, and the oldest, a sister, who is 8 years older.

Ms. A. feels close to her sister, and says that she was like a second mother to her when they were growing up. They formed a mutual support system. She does not have much of a relationship with her brothers.

Family History of Illness

Alcoholism is the family disease. In addition to her father's being alcoholic, her maternal and paternal grandfathers also were alcoholic, her sister married an alcoholic, and both of her brothers drink heavily.

Personal History

Early Years

Ms. A. does not recall her earliest years. During grammar school, she remembers feeling as though she did not fit in with the other kids. She remembers being teased by the other children and having only a few friends. In junior high and high school, she was a very good student, but very shy. Her feelings of not fitting in continued and she used studying as a way to escape from dealing with other people. She did not have a boyfriend. She said that she never liked the boys who liked her, only the ones who were unavailable.

Ms. A. says that she walked around scared all the time because her father was so unpredictable.

College, Work, and Graduate School

Ms. A. was afraid to go away to school, and instead attended a small college near her home, because she thought she would feel safer in "a nice controlled environment." She was introverted and depressed and had difficulty with adjusting and making friends. She entered therapy during that time and changed considerably, becoming more confident, outgoing, and independent. She stopped drinking for a year and began to separate from her family. During this time, Ms. A. began to date and to have sex.

After graduation, she worked as a bookkeeper and, for the first time, was financially independent of her family. She decided to go to graduate school to get a master's degree in accounting. She began to think that she would be happier living away from her family.

Ms. A.'s parents disapproved of her decision to go away to business school. They wanted her to become a teacher in the local elementary school, marry a local man, and live nearby, as her mother had done. When Ms. A. insisted on going to school out of town and pursuing her ambitions, her parents withdrew all emotional and financial support and predicted that she would be a failure in life.

Ms. A. was not able to get into a good graduate school because she suffered from severe test anxiety, which was exacerbated by her conflicts with her parents, and she did not do well on her entrance exam. She persisted and eventually was accepted by a small school in New York. She moved to the city, found a job, and successfully completed her M.B.A. degree. During this time, none of her family, except for her sister, visited her or offered her any help. She and the sister continued to talk on the telephone regularly and my client frequently visited her.

She made the transition from home by becoming obsessively absorbed in and dependent on a succession of men, and lived with some of them. All of her relationships had essentially the same pattern: she would quickly form an intense dependency on a man, and the ups and down of their relationship and how he treated her would become her major focus in life.

Sometimes Ms. A. would call in sick and stay home from work because she had been out late drinking the night before. She says that she literally feels ill, as though she has the flu, when things are not going well with one of her relationships. Although Ms. A. says that she enjoys sex with these men and usually reaches orgasm, it is clear that sex is not the main attraction for her. She needs to have an attentive man in her life in order to feel good about herself.

Ms. A. supported herself in graduate school by working and taking school loans. When she became ill and needed money for doctors' bills, she did not ask her parents for financial help because she was sure that their response would be: "You made your bed, so lie in it!"

Mental Status Examination

The patient was appropriately dressed. Although she was obviously nervous, she seemed friendly, open, and appealing. Her psychomotor function, her speech, and her thought processes were normal. Her perceptions were normal as well. No hallucinations were present. Her memory seemed intact, her fund of information seemed average, and her orientation was good. Intellectually, she seemed bright, but insecure about herself.

She reported that her moods tended to be highly variable, depending on the state of her current relationship. She was not clinically depressed and had no suicidal or homicidal ideation.

Her insight was fair, but her judgment was compromised by her need to act out defensively with alcohol and men to manage her feelings. She fantasized that meeting the right man would solve her problems.

In session, her affect sometimes was not appropriate to the material she was discussing. She often laughed and made light of situations that obviously were painful for her. Her manner seemed to say, "Isn't this silly of me?" and invited others to take her less seriously than she deserved.

Clinical Diagnostic Formulation

This patient presents an interesting diagnostic picture: she appears to have the day-to-day self-sufficiency of a schizoid patient, the clinging and acting-out defenses of a borderline patient, and the sensitivity to slights of a narcissistic patient.

Schizoid Disorder of the Self

In support of her having a schizoid disorder of the self is her remarkable self-sufficiency and her difficulty with trusting others. She applied for welfare rather than ask her friends or family for help. In this light, her alternation between periods of aloneness during which she obsessively studied and periods of obsessive absorption in a man could be seen as manifestations of the schizoid dilemma: "My choice is between isolation and despair and a master–slave relationship in which I am totally subservient to the needs of the other."

Events in her early life could support this interpretation. Around her father, she only existed to listen to him pontificate. Her mother seemed oblivious to and uninterested in who she was or what her needs were. Acceptance in the family was contingent on her satisfying her mother's desire to have an obedient and religious daughter.

In session, however, Ms. A. did not behave in ways typical of most schizoid patients. She seemed comfortable with expressing spontaneous emotion in front of me, she quickly formed a positive transference acting out, and I never felt that intrusiveness or appropriation was a significant issue for her.

Borderline Disorder of the Self

Ms. A.'s chaotic personal life could also be seen as typical for someone suffering from a borderline disorder of the self. She had difficulty managing herself and her emotions; she tended to see the people in her life in very black-and-white terms, and she used many acting-out defenses. She had the typically borderline difficulty with organizing herself enough to meet her basic needs of getting enough sleep and having enough clothing to wear.

Thus her bad feelings about herself, her sense of panic as she tried to support herself to individuate, and her sense of her mother as being angry, critical, and withdrawing could be seen as typical manifestations of the part-self and part-object representations of the "withdrawing or aggressive part-object relationship unit." Formulated in this fashion, her therapists and her sister would become the "good mother" in the "rewarding or libidinal part objects relations unit" and she "the good little girl" who got taken care of and loved in exchange for passivity and compliance. Certainly she was very compliant in her relationship with both of her parents. Her difficulty in leaving home to go to college would, at the deepest level, represent the borderline fear that, "If I separate from my mother and activate myself, either she or I will go crazy or die."

Narcissistic Disorder of the Self

Ms. A. did not present with a typical exhibitionistic narcissistic disorder of the self. She was openly insecure about almost everything about herself, from her looks to her education. And I never felt afraid of offending her as I often do with exhibitionistic narcissistic patients. She frequently laughed at her own foibles and she was always open to feedback from me. However, she did have certain features that argued for a possible closet narcissistic diagnosis.

In her first session with me, she had described herself as "the mirror of whatever anyone else thinks of me." This sounds like a clear expression of the defensively fused split self and object relations units of the narcissistic disorder. In this light, my patient sought therapy with me at this time because she needed to fuse with an idealized omnipotent other in order to feel potent enough to pass her licensing exam. Her relationships with men would be about the same thing: desperate attempts to fuse and receive narcissistic supplies.

Also possibly supporting a narcissistic diagnosis were her constant complaints about how overworked and unappreciated she was at whatever job she was holding. She invariably complained that she was treated like a nothing. This could be the result of an underlying sense of grandiosity and entitlement that made her feel slighted when she was not given the recognition she felt was her due, combined with her reluctance to assert herself and be in the spotlight, which is often found in the closet narcissist.

Posttraumatic Stress Disorder

The patient's sexual acting out and the alcoholic father raise the possibility that she is suffering from PTSD as well. Although she says that she has no memories of sexual abuse and that she personally was never hit, the tension level in her household may have been so great as to be traumatic for her, or there may have been incidents of sexual abuse that she does not remember and is reenacting with men. In further support of a PTSD diagnosis is her report that she walks around "scared" all the time.

Course of Treatment

After considering the whole picture, I was fairly certain that this patient did not have a schizoid disorder of the self. And although she had some features that could support a diagnosis of closet narcissistic disorder of the self, she had many more that seemed to point to her having a borderline disorder of the self. For this reason, I decided to treat her for a borderline disorder, while keeping in mind that she might also be suffering from PTSD. I used confrontations of the denied destructiveness of her acting-out behaviors as my main therapeutic tool. Here are some examples of my confrontations and the patient's responses.

I began by confronting Ms. A.'s pattern of coming late to sessions:

Patient: (*Rushing in 10 minutes late*) I'm sorry I'm late. I lost track of time. I stayed up till 6 a.m. studying, and I've felt sick and tired all day.

Therapist: You said that coming to therapy was very important to you and was a financial sacrifice. Why do you cheat yourself by coming late and exhausted?

Patient: I don't have enough time for myself. I'm always running from one thing to another. I don't even take lunch most days. Besides (*laughing*) I guess I'd rather be sick now than sick after my exam because I failed.

As with the example, my confrontations were often met with rationalizations and excuses.

Frequently, Ms. A. felt that her boyfriends mistreated her, but she never said anything to them directly about her feelings. Instead, she tended to withdraw or retaliate. I began to confront her reluctance to speak up for herself. The following is a typical example.

Patient: (*Talking about how badly she felt a boyfriend had treated her and how she was planning not to return his calls*) I am angry and I want to hurt him back because he has hurt me. I would never treat anyone the way he treats me. It makes me feel bad about me when he only calls me for a date at the last minute and then doesn't want to pay for my dinner.

Therapist: Why does it make you feel bad about you?

Patient: Because maybe there is something wrong with me. Maybe I'm too needy. I don't know what is normal. I need you to tell me that it is not me, or else I feel that I did something wrong or I'm expecting too much.

Therapist: You seem to feel that you have no right to decide for yourself how you want to be treated. Why is that?

Patient: I'm too afraid of losing him or showing him how much I care. I don't want to give him that. I'm so hurt that I'd rather just not return his phone calls and find someone else.

Therapist: This has happened to you over and over with a bunch of different men. If you don't like the way someone is treating you, why keep starting over? Why wouldn't you say something to him directly, instead of just fuming in silence and withdrawing?

Patient: (*Laughing*) You mean I can do that?

Soon after this session, Ms. A. began to complain to her boyfriend about his treatment of her and in general became more open with him about her feelings. This looked like therapeutic progress on the surface, and partly it may have been, but I did not totally trust it. I was concerned that compliance might also be playing a significant role in the changes she was making. Now, instead of trying to please her boyfriends and do what they told her to do, was she doing what she thought I thought she should do?

Acts of self-activation were promptly followed by physical and mental collapse during which the patient developed flulike symptoms and went to bed. My confrontations did not significantly affect the frequency of this behavior, nor did she seem interested in exploring it. The following interchange is typical of many.

Patient: I finally got my stuff in to the exam people, but I've been feeling sick since then, I got bad stomach cramps at work. I had a fever and it felt like I had the flu. I left work early and went home to bed. That's when I called you to change the appointment.

Therapist: Your attempts to move forward in life often seem to be followed by your feeling sick. This seems to be one of those times. You take a step forward and then one back.

Patient: That isn't fair. I know that I do that sometimes, but this time I really was sick.

After six months of using confrontation as my main therapeutic tool, I reevaluated the situation. On the plus side: Ms. A.'s life was going better in certain practical ways. She had passed her licensing exam, and she had found herself a new apartment and a better job. However, on the minus side, she still managed her life so that she usually felt exhausted and abused, she continued to distract herself with men, she still had not seriously looked for a job as an accountant, and she was as dependent as ever on others for feedback and direction.

In addition, certain narcissistic issues seemed to be coming to the foreground. Ms. A. spoke more and more frequently about how she did not feel good enough to be a professional and about her pervasive feelings of inferiority. It was obvious that she had difficulty retaining any good feelings about herself in the absence of positive feedback and encouragement. In summary, she was making certain external changes in her life, but internally she seemed not much different from how she was when she entered therapy with me.

I reconsidered my diagnosis of Ms. A. If she had a closet narcissistic disorder and not a borderline, then the picture I was seeing made more sense. Her external functioning had improved while she was in therapy because she was able to fuse with an idealized omnipotent object—the therapist. She used her projections to fuel herself and to counteract the harsh, attacking, and devaluing internal object of her aggressive fused part unit and the concomitant sense of herself as inadequate, fragmented, unworthy, and unentitled.

I decided to test this hypothesis by switching from confrontation to mirroring interpretations of her narcissistic vulnerability. There was a striking change in her reactions. Almost immediately, the affect tone of our sessions deepened. This can be clearly seen in the following example where I interpreted how she continually focused on the other because focusing on herself and her own feelings made her feel vulnerable.

Patient: I haven't had my lunch yet. I'm so exhausted I'll probably end up taking a cab that I can't afford back to work. I could lie down now and go to sleep right here. I have to stop scheduling things solely to please my managers, but when I don't get something done that they want me to do, I feel irresponsible and like I haven't worked hard enough.

Therapist: It is so difficult for you to focus on your own needs because it makes you feel so vulnerable to criticism that you attempt to soothe yourself by trying to please your bosses, even though it means exhausting yourself.

Patient: (*Beginning to cry.*) I'm so afraid of complaints. At night I lie awake thinking about the things I haven't done and worrying . . . I feel overwhelmed about prioritizing. It is very difficult for me to organize myself. I feel I should be able to do everything perfectly.

This led to memories of how perfectly organized her mother insisted they be and how the patient would "beat herself up" for not being organized enough.

Another example.

> **Patient:** (*After failing an out-of-state licensing exam*) Why is accomplishing this so tied to my self-esteem? Why can't I be satisfied with the licensing exam I've already passed? It is like when a guy rejects me. I reject myself. Why doesn't my boyfriend feel this way? He failed his licensing exam twice. (At *this point, she stopped talking about herself and started talking about her boyfriend. I brought this to her attention with an interpretation.*)
>
> **Therapist:** It is so painful for you to stay in touch with these feelings about yourself that you protect yourself by focusing on your boyfriend.
>
> **Patient:** Yes. It is really hard for me to keep the focus on myself. I begin to feel as though there is something wrong with me. Then it's like I need someone else to make me feel like I'm okay. Do you think I'm on the right track here?
>
> **Therapist:** As you try to focus on yourself, painful feelings of self-doubt come up and you soothe yourself by changing the subject or looking to the external world for validation—as you just did with me.
>
> **Patient:** Yes. It dawned on me over the weekend that I'm coming to therapy and looking for you to validate me because I don't have the power within me to validate myself. (*At this point*, *Ms. A. starts to cry, then sits quietly, tearing up a tissue.*) I have too much feeling, so I try to avoid it by laughing or changing the subject. This reminds me of how I would act around my family after a fight. I would just be quiet and sit there waiting for the feelings to pass.

In the following sessions, as I continued to interpret Ms. A.'s various ways of avoiding staying with her feelings and self-activating, she began to do more of the work herself. She reported thinking about her therapy between sessions and consciously utilizing what she had learned here. In session she began to turn to me less and less for validation. She began to explore her pervasive sense of inferiority and her need to please others. She did this with affect and often with associated memories from childhood.

Ms. A. had slowly begun to develop a more realistic and positive view of herself. This has translated into a burst of self-activation during which, for the first time, she has seriously and effectively begun to look for a job as an accountant. She has had three interviews, which is in sharp contrast with her past record of never having gone for a job interview in her field because she felt like a fraud.

As she went on interviews and did well, her self-confidence increased and her need for her boyfriend's constant attention and approval dramatically decreased. She reported feeling more independent and secure as she realized that most of her fears about accountancy firms' automatically rejecting her were unrealistic projections of her own sense of inadequacy. She is getting more sleep and is realistically limiting the number of hours she works. As she recently said: "I need to make sure that I take care of myself and put my needs first. If I don't, no one else will."

Conclusion

It is worthwhile at this point to look back at this case that so dramatically presented as a borderline. The patient had:

- extreme difficulty separating from her family and making the transition to college
- an inability to be alone, coupled with a constant panicky search for men to whom to cling
- a pattern of intense, chaotic relationships;
- impulsive acting-out behaviors: drinking, sex, missing work
- difficulties with the basics of self-maintenance: getting

enough sleep, cleaning the house, making sure that she had warm-enough clothing

- a presenting complaint that was typically borderline: she felt extremely anxious about leaving the structured environment of graduate school and having to self-activate and make her own decisions about her future career

On the basis of the above, it is likely that many therapists would have made the same mistake that I did and diagnose and treat this patient as having a borderline disorder. Her compliant response would mistakenly be taken as evidence that she was getting better. Probably many closet narcissistic disorders are misdiagnosed in this way and, as a result, do not reach their full therapeutic potential. This case clearly illustrates why it is important to keep in mind that ultimately it is the patient's intrapsychic structure as it manifests in the transference acting out and in the patient's reactions to our interventions that should determine the diagnosis and appropriate treatment, not a description of his or her behavior.

CASE 4:

CLOSET NARCISSISTIC DISORDER OR NARCISSISTIC DEFENSES AGAINST A SCHIZOID DISORDER?*

Ms. G., a 23-year-old Jewish woman, works as a research assistant at a New York City medical center. She is tall, studious looking, and rather plain in appearance, with no apparent sense of style. The impression is of someone who has no interest in appearing attractive or being noticed.

*Case courtesy Arlene Hahn, C.S.W.

Chief Complaint

The patient stated, "I've been depressed for a couple of months, but have felt better the last few weeks. It's a pattern that I would like to break."

History of Present Illness

Ms. G. experiences long periods of "breaking down" and short, intense periods of "falling apart." She cries and doesn't feel like dealing with anything. A recent precipitant was her roommate's withdrawal from their friendship. The patient considered her a good friend and is distressed over this loss. Although able to pinpoint a precipitant, she doesn't think her behavior is normal since she can't remember feeling good for more than two days at a time during recent years. She has always been moody, but manages to keep it under control and to not let it affect her work life. She tends to be preoccupied with herself, feeling better when she is less self-absorbed and is involved with activities. She enjoys school, reading, and writing, and plays the flute. The patient recalls always being self-conscious, and since childhood she always worried about what others thought of her. She felt different, more intelligent than most of her peers, and had a lifelong struggle fitting in with and connecting to others, but sees socializing as a "liferaft."

Ms. G. denied any history of substance abuse; physical or sexual abuse was not reported. The patient has symptoms of depression, and major affective disorder was later ruled out.

History of Previous Psychiatric Illness

When the patient was 15, her mother initiated therapy because of their conflict over the patient's attempts to establish her independence. Her mother was upset by the amount of time Ms. G. was spending with her boyfriend.

Family History

Her mother, age 48, was described as intelligent and supportive of the patient's intellectual abilities. The patient only had conflicts with her mother while in high school. She wanted to please her mother, complying with her wishes and keeping out of her way.

She described her father, age 49, as a brilliant surgeon. The patient is uncomfortable with having similar interests and possibly following in his footsteps. He often retreats to his study and has a tendency to interview rather than to talk to people.

Ms. G. thinks that both parents encouraged her intellectual elitism, distinguishing her from her peers. As a result, she thought she was a genius. She thought that the fact that she called her parents by their first names exemplified an elevated status. The patient believes they were good parents and doesn't understand why she becomes depressed when returning home for visits.

Ms. G. is the younger of two children. Her sister, who is four years older, was a stubborn child, an average student who was always at odds with their mother. The patient thinks this increased her parents' expectations of her. The patient found their fighting very upsetting and spent a great deal of time alone in her room reading, studying, and writing in a journal. When her sister became difficult, she behaved perfectly by offering to help her mother with chores and liked getting attention for being the good child.

There were no other significant caretakers, and no family history of illness.

Past Personal History

Ages 0–3, none.

Ages 3–5, The patient recalls no difficulty in separating for kindergarten.

The patient recalls feeling different from the other kids. She didn't have many friends and was convinced of her brilliance. At age 8, she asked her mother if she was a genius. She liked fantasy and was a voracious reader.

Ms. G. was unhappy at school, but when transferred to a gifted program, she felt more comfortable with other "strange and gifted" children like herself. Her interests included playing the piano and flute, and reading.

Adolescence

The patient made friends more easily in high school and had a boyfriend for three years. Her mother was disturbed by their relationship and she thinks that she didn't want her to grow up. This was the first time Ms. G. went "ballistic," arguing with her mother. She wanted her independence and wouldn't compromise. The patient didn't act out in other ways and felt she was still a good kid.

Her boyfriend was stubborn as well; they often butted heads, but he was otherwise a nice guy and they shared similar interests. Sexual contact was minimal and limited to kissing.

College and Postadolescence

The patient attended college in New York City, where she had a small group of friends. She felt she didn't really have a grip on being there until her senior year, when she began to enjoy it. She had several crushes during her college years and fantasized about them a lot, and also wrote in her journal. When she revealed her feelings to one man, he reacted with shock and detachment. It was distressing for her to have loving feelings toward someone who didn't really understand who she was. The other men had similar problems with attachment. She still fantasizes about these relationships. She has never had sexual intercourse.

Ms. G. spent her junior year in Israel. She considers this the happiest time in her life. During the summer prior to her return, she worked on a kibbutz and had a feeling of belonging. She spent much of her time observing relationships, and felt more comfortable with people than ever before.

The patient made a few women friends at college and became best friends with her roommate. After graduation, they shared an apartment, but their relationship deteriorated as her friend withdrew and became critical of her. The patient is suffering from this loss and wants very much to repair the relationship.

Following her graduation from college where her major was premed, she took the job as a research assistant at the medical center. She has an entry-level position and is bored with all the clerical work.

She plans to be an orthopedist, but has not yet applied to a medical school.

Ms. G. has an impoverished social life and spends her time alone, reading, fantasizing about relationships, and writing in her journal. She feels awkward and self-conscious in social situations, is rarely able to stop focusing on her own behavior, and at times feels like an alien and does not know how to interact socially by making small talk.

Clinical Diagnostic Formulation

The patient presented with a confusing diagnostic picture. It was unclear as to whether she had a closet narcissistic disorder or was exhibiting narcissistic defenses against a schizoid disorder. Her impoverished object relations and detachment appeared schizoid, but her grandiosity was pervasive. There were many incongruities. Was her lifelong grandiosity and feelings of superiority an attempt to establish an acceptable distance from the object or was it a way of enhancing her grandiose self?

She expressed a strong desire to connect with others, has impoverished object relations, and sees relationships as a liferaft. She is socially awkward and unable to communicate and interact effectively. Are these the alien feelings of a schizoid disorder or the self-esteem issues of a narcissistic disorder?

She utilized fantasy and journal writing, focusing on relationships with men as a defense. Was this a way to soothe herself or the compromise of a schizoid disorder? She felt rejected when a man in whom she was interested didn't understand who she was. Was this the narcissistic requirement for one-mindedness?

Ms. G. utilized classic schizoid descriptions like "liferaft" and "alien," spending a great deal of time alone. She also expressed classic narcissistic concerns of falling apart and didn't strike me as particularly self-reliant. In addition, her history of family relationships sounded idealized and more benign than a schizoid disorder.

Was the patient seeking therapy to feel better or was it out of a desperate need for attachment? Following the initial evaluation, I decided to utilize the therapeutic interventions to test for and confirm a diagnosis. I decided to test first for schizoid disorder. I was concerned that a mirroring interpretation of her narcissistic vulnerability and defense might be intolerable for a person with schizoid disorder, who would experience me as appropriating and intrusive.

Course of Treatment

The following excerpts demonstrate my initial interventions and attempts to confirm the diagnosis of schizoid. I began by interpreting Ms. G.'s need for safety in relationships.

The patient described the man from college whom she still saw occasionally. She stated, "In college he was someone I could fool around with without any risk. He's not romantic, but that doesn't disqualify him. He's not the first guy that I've been attracted to and then got little in return. We never even kissed. But it's the first time that I'm not just having a dialogue with myself. Yet I'm concerned that if I see him more often, my feelings will diminish. If I were a normal woman, I would just have a fling."

Therapist: It seems to me that you have a desire to get closer but it feels risky, so you choose men who are unlikely to pursue you, and then turn away in order to feel safe.

Patient: It's more his problem than mine. He's further back in this round than me.

The patient's reaction was defensive, focusing on the other.

Over the next couple of sessions, I made similar safety interpretations, and each time the patient responded defensively. I had difficulty connecting with Ms. G., felt afraid to intrude on her, and was careful about giving her space. I thought my countertransference was indicative of her having a schizoid disorder. However, as I became more aware of my feelings, I realized that my concerns were more about hurting her, bursting her bubble, and making her angry at me. I felt dismissed and devalued, and was preoccupied with finding the perfect interpretation. My countertransference provided some evidence that the patient had a narcissistic disorder rather than a schizoid disorder. However, I wanted clinical evidence of the patient's one-mindedness before changing the diagnosis. The patient then helped by essentially diagnosing herself. The following took place.

Patient: I don't trust first impressions. I can't just talk to people. It's like a social learning disability. I rely on work and school but eventually I have to interact and rule out people I don't respect and to whom I feel superior. I'm afraid of what I'll think of people. My expectations are high. I'm suspicious, critical, and a snob. I like to observe.

Therapist: It's my impression that as you try to connect, you start to feel vulnerable, and then you are critical and de value in order to protect yourself.

Patient: I've been thinking since last week. *We're* only half right abut being safe. I'm as afraid of what I'll think of people, my expectations are high, and I don't like being let down. I expect people to follow a script and I guess wrong. I'm a snob and my standards are high for who I want as friends.

Ms. G. presented evidence of one-mindedness and fusion with the therapist by use of the word "we." A schizoid individual would never use "we" in this way. I changed my diagnosis to closet narcissistic disorder and my approach to incorporating mirroring interpretations of narcissistic vulnerability and defense.

The following vignettes demonstrate the change in the patient's response to my interpretations, confirmation of the diagnosis, and the beginning of the patient's feeling understood, enabling her to utilize therapy to work on her severe deficits in object relations and self-esteem.

Patient: I'd like to seem less strange to people or less obviously unhappy. A man at work likes me but he can't get past my awkwardness and strange behaviors. He's trying to figure me out and reach me, but I'm not good with people, I'm not entertaining enough, and I can't communicate clearly.

Therapist: You have such painful feelings about yourself, and think others feel that way about you too, that you protect yourself by keeping yourself difficult to understand and hard to reach.

Patient: But if I get clear, I don't see how it will help. (*Patient cries.*) What's clear about me isn't good enough and will keep people away. It seems like the only option at the time. I'm trying to keep things I don't want people to see covered up. Why am I like this? I act like my parents were taken away when I was 3. It doesn't seem fair; I had a perfectly stable childhood and yet I'm not able to deal with people.

This set the stage for addressing the patient's self-esteem issues and her projections. In another session, the patient reported an incident with her sister in which she found herself agreeing with her rather than saying what she was thinking.

Patient: I told her what she wanted to hear. When there are restrictions on what I say, I can't think straight, I'm no good unedited. Often I have no words and can't talk straight. I need to have everything weighed out and processed before I can hold a conversation.

Therapist: It's so painful for you to say something that might not be accepted that you protect yourself by editing, revising, and losing your spontaneity.

Patient: Yes, I wonder what would happen if I just said what I feel. I don't know how to make that change. I figure out ways to avoid, or sidestep, or tell people what they want to hear. I defend against feeling that someone doesn't like me and doubt myself.

It became clear that the patient's withdrawal from relationships was her ultimate defense in warding off rejection and fortifying her narcissistic defenses of idealization and denial in order to defend against narcissistic injury and fragmentation. Her withdrawal had nothing to do with the fear of appropriation and interpersonal space issues of the schizoid.

The intrapsychic structure of the patient's closet narcissistic disorder consisted of two fused object relations part-units with a major investment in idealizing the omnipotent object, basking in its glow to regulate her grandiosity. The object-representation of the grandiose self/omnipotent object part-unit was perfect and brilliant. The self-representation was special, unique, and a "genius."

The patient is unable to consistently maintain this defensive unit and the underlying empty/aggressive part-unit is provoked and is more pervasive in the treatment. The object-representation of this part-unit is harsh and attacking. The self-representation is unattractive, unappealing, awkward, inadequate, and an "alien." The linking affect of the abandonment depression is falling apart.

As therapy progressed, Ms. G. became more aware and was less defensive, displaying more affect and focusing more on her "self." She is less socially awkward and is beginning to enjoy more social situations. She is less moody and is better at managing the times she becomes depressed. She is dressing more attractively and has applied to medical school. She has made a few attempts at dating and is now addressing her fears more directly.

Part III

Treatment

Chapters 6–8 present a complete report (process notes) of six years (575 sessions) of successful psychoanalytic psychotherapy twice a week of a 35-year-old single man whose chief complaints were difficulties at work and in relations with women. This seemingly simple surface presentation became extraordinarily complex over time as the complete diagnosis emerged, that is, dissociative and closet narcissistic defenses against oedipal conflict and a neurosis:

Each chapter describes the gradual working through of a deeper level of defenses:

- Chapter 6: Dissociative defenses against mourning the loss of a father.
- Chapter 7: Closet narcissistic defenses against the abandonment depression with the mother.
- Chapter 8: Neurotic defenses against oedipal castration conflict with the mother and father.

The death theme of the abandonment depression (i.e., loss of the object in the preoedipal phase) is reinforced by the loss of the father in the early oedipal phase, which, in turn, reinforces the basic conflict of the oedipal phase—death by retribution for the triumph of oedipal wishes. However, the difference in the content of the working through in the two phases is clearly illustrated. The therapist's guide through this psychopathological maze was to focus constantly on defense.

Chapter Six

Working Through Dissociative Defenses and Mourning the Loss of a Father

Mr. L., a 35-year-old, short, blond, slender, meticulously groomed banker, moderately anxious and mildly depressed, articulated his problem with very little intervention on my part.

Chief Complaint

The patient reported, "I have a vague anxiety, a lack of sense of authenticity, as if I can't be myself and be successful and I'm tired of living life on the defensive. I never feel like I'm living directly or free and I never feel satisfied. I have a lack of entitlement or a lack of courage to follow through and don't feel I deserve anything. I feel I'm cheating and I'm constantly afraid that bad things will happen, and they generally do." (He gives an excellent description of his difficulty with his sense of self, that is, self-image and self-activation.)

Precipitating Stress

Mr. L. reported that in the last 18 months, he had suffered three severe losses: two of his best friends were killed in automobile accidents and he had recently lost so much money in the market that he might not be able to afford to keep his apartment. He elaborated on his difficulty with real self-activation in work and relationships.

History of Present Illness: Work

"In college I majored in acting and theater and minored in economics, and worked at my acting. I did fairly well.

"When I graduated, I continued my study at an acting school in New York City in the company of many who are now famous, and I also had a private acting coach. My coach eventually lost interest in me and I panicked about not having enough money, and so 10 years ago at the age of 25, I left the theater world and took a job with a bank in order to make a salary. I did well until recently. But even so, I didn't like it. I had to force myself. I procrastinated, but I'm fearfully obsessed with not having enough money, which I depend on to validate my sense of self.

"On the other hand, I feel guilty about not doing what I could in the theater because I think I have a lot of talent. I'm also a perfectionist, but I have to force myself to do the work."

Relationships with Women

"I'm addicted to women and money as a way of measuring my sense of self. I have a fantasy of the ideal perfect woman and I'm afraid that if I marry a real one, I will miss out on the perfect one, who will probably show up among the guests on my wedding day.

"Until 10 years ago, I dated older women. The relationships would usually last two years and then we would break up. I've been with my current girlfriend for five years, and have lived with her for two years. She initiated the relationship and really has carried it for me. I should marry her, but I'm still keeping my options open for the perfect woman, although I feel I love her and she is awfully good to me.

"My goal or vision is to live life authentically, to be plugged into it, to marry the perfect woman and become such a good actor that I will validate myself."

History

"I was born in the Midwest, the youngest of four, with an older brother and two older sisters. I was okay until age 3 ½ when my father was killed in an automobile accident. My mother was terribly depressed, cried a lot, so my development was suffused in sorrow. Mother had rages if we disobeyed and beat us with a belt. On the other hand, I was the baby of the family. I grew up among women, but when I started school, my mother went back to work as a teacher, and I resented it.

"However, despite the rages, Mother also seemed to encourage our growth and finally, when I was 18, I became curious about what my father had been like and what my relationship with him had been. I did well in high school and went away to college, after which I came to New York."

The patient denied any vegetative signs of depression and/or any abuse of alcohol or drugs. There was no evidence of an affective disorder.

Intrapsychic Structure

It's helpful to consider the intrapsychic structure as consisting of two layers: an initial layer and a later layer that emerged as a result of treatment. The initial layer was regressive, defensive, and narcissistic. The later layer was neurotic. The initial layer consisted of a defensive fused grandiose self—omnipotent object-representation with a condensed (i.e., his mother and father) preoedipal omnipotent object-representation that was idealized, was all powerful, and provided admiration for being mirrored by the self-representation. This representation was projected onto others, but particularly onto women, as a way of regulating the sense of self. The grandiose self-representation was of being unique, great, special by giving up real self-activation, catering to the needs of the idealized object, and basking in the glow of the object's response. The affect was of feeling special, admired, adored.

The aggressive fused unit consisted of a harsh attacking object-representation that was literally experienced as an internal voice whenever the patient attempted self-activation. The self-representation was of being gutted, dead, empty, inadequate. The affect linking these two representations was predominately the abandonment depression characterized by fears of death because of loss of the object.

This structure formed a regressive narcissistic defense against an underlying neurotic structure, complete with sexual and affectionate feelings for the mother and competition with and fear of retribution from the father. This aspect of the problem did not reveal itself until the dissociative and regressive narcissistic defenses had been worked through.

The condensed and preoedipal omnipotent object-representation of the father was initially hidden by the dissociative defense and did not emerge until those defenses had been worked through. The representation of the mother as a sexual object and of the father as an agent of competitive retributions did not emerge until the narcissistic defenses were worked through.

Clinical Impression

After three interviews, my clinical impression was that of a closet narcissistic disorder with idealization and focus on the object—women, others, and money—as a way of regulating a sense of self with impairment of the real self and self-activation both at work and in relationships with women. The profound importance of the dissociation defense and the neurotic conflict emerged later. The patient also had severe dissociative defenses against the loss of the father and secondarily reinforced the need to focus on the mother to help her manage her depression at the loss.

It would appear that Mr. L. had had an exhibitionistic grandiose self in early childhood, but, as often happens, the severe traumas and lack of support impelled a defensive reversal of emotional investment from the grandiose self to the omnipotent object, thereby producing a closet narcissistic personality disorder.

It would be necessary to work through both types of defenses, but it was unclear as to which would come first. The loss of the father occurred at that crucial stage when the patient was shifting major emotional investment from the mother to the father to sustain and consolidate the emerging self, and the traumatic loss caused him to dissociate all feelings about his father and the sense of real self associated with him.

An argument might be made that this is denial, not dissociation. In my view, the complete exclusion from consciousness of affect and memory argues for dissociation. The mother's collapse and need for support reinforced the loss, not only at the time, but later when real-life events seemed to afflict the mother recurrently throughout Mr. L.'s developmental years—that is, at each stage when he attempted self-activation, the mother fell prey to another trauma. This led to an almost phobic perspective on self-activation—if he activates the real self, bad things will happen. The nidus of this perspective lies much deeper in his feeling that he was responsible for his father's death and his sense of real self died at the same time. Overcoming the dissociative defenses led to mourning the loss, which allowed him to recapture and refocus on the sense of real self, which led to a focus on working through the narcissistic defenses around work and relationships with women, which, in turn, led to a working through of the underlying neurotic conflict against which the closet narcissistic personality disorder had been a defense.

He began therapy once a week for one month and then changed to twice-a-week sessions. He is the only patient in 40 years of practice who could do this level of work on a twice-a-week basis. It usually requires sessions at least three times a week.

Psychotherapy

Mirroring Interpretation of Narcissistic Vulnerability Overcomes Dissociative Defenses

First Month

After focusing on how he had compromised himself too much and how he must try to be who he is and do what he wants to do, he reported a kind of vague but deep sorrow and disappointment at the rejection by his acting coach and mentor, with some thoughts about feeling depressed about the death of his father. He followed through in the next session: "I drifted away from acting to deal with the pain of rejection by my mentor. I can remember wanting to know if my father had loved me, but I can remember only one time he touched me. I remember one scene with him in which he gave me a wrench, of which I was very proud. It was like having one's heart broken and exalted at the same time."

He began the next session by turning to me, "Should I start or should you?" I made the following interpretation: "The last two sessions you seemed to focus on yourself, which led to painful feelings of loss about your mentor and your father. It seems now you feel a need to focus on me as a way of soothing those painful feelings."

Mr. L. elaborated his idealization defense: "I love the greater authority to tell me what to do. I turn off into religion and prayer. I like to be led, like to be given the courage to do things by others. (The omnipotent object-representation.) I'm still trying to be more myself in my work, to use my instincts to do what is me. I think I avoided it in order to avoid suffering."

He then reported more feelings of loss from his past: "As the youngest child, I was bossed around, but I was also pampered and I wasn't tested. I had no courage to suffer for my convictions. My mother's suffering overwhelmed her and me. I still keep a lot of fantasy women in my head, and this hurts my real relationship with women. It sacrifices my integrity. The death of my father had a severe effect on my mother. My mother lost control. At one point, she had to be taken to the state hospital, saying we were driving her crazy. I use my acting to express sadness, not joy. I was afraid of losing her. My loving mother turned into a monster and I felt scared and guilty."

I suggested at this point that perhaps the loss of the mother had as great an impact as the loss of the father. In retrospect, this was a premature interpretation.

In the next session, he ignored my interpretation, that is, he reported being depressed at seeing the price he had paid for focusing on others. "This is my time to be tested, this is the measure of me. One day this week, I had a brief quiet sense of confidence that things will be okay, which seemed powerful, and then went away." (The beginning of a therapeutic alliance?)

I now again interpreted that this difficulty in focusing on himself seemed to be attributable to the need to avoid focusing on the feelings of loss associated with that focus—and that this feeling of loss seemed to be associated as much with his mother as with his father. Clearly, caught in countertransference, I had not taken the hint that this was premature. He now briefly complied, talking about his mother's sorrow and her angry outbursts. "But if I was angry, she attacked me so I had to turn it into myself, into sorrow. Maybe between ages 3 and 7, I may have lost my mother to her sorrow, the idea scares me."

"When I get really involved in what I'm doing, I get anxiety attacks. (Self-activation leads to anxiety.) I've been pushing myself to get into acting again, to do what I care about, and also I'm trying to decide on my own more about bank investments without seeking others' advice, which is a real breakthrough."

However, despite this change in behavior, he reported no consequent emotional self-acknowledgment. When I brought this to his attention through mirroring interpretation, his feelings of guilt and worthlessness emerged and he burst into tears and said, "That would mean I'm worthy and I won't believe that. I don't feel worthy and I don't know why. I feel so guilty about my mother's threatening to leave because she felt I was driving her crazy."

Feelings of Worthlessness and Guilt About the Father's Death

The interpretation began to open up the dissociative defense associated with the loss of his sense of self. He reported in the next session, "I can't believe I'm worthy. After the last session, I tried to focus on this feeling. Maybe I am getting a second chance. I'm grieving as if someone died. Between ages 3 and 4, I remember going to four funerals—my father's, my grandfather's, and a neighbor's, even a baby in the neighborhood. I think I'm the one who died, some part of me."

At this point, the patient was sobbing. "I should have done something about my father's death. I think it's my fault. I've been doing time. At home this week, I cried so hard, and then I turned it into laughter for 15 minutes. I was astonished. I never would have believed all this. I've been doing time. I have to forgive myself. I have to feel compassion for that kid.

"My mother used to say that if my father were alive, I wouldn't get away with so much. Maybe I was glad that he died. Then I felt that the one who was so good to me was gone; was it my mother or my father? I felt myself expanding from being so cramped. The laughter felt so good and deep.

"All this took about two hours with a great feeling of relief and being exonerated and charges dropped, and then things will be okay."

He then reported a dream: "I was snorkeling, got too far away from shore, and saw a cloud coming."

Free Association: "It was an anxiety dream; there was disaster coming, I was trapped and couldn't get out."

I interpreted that he was trapped between his need to focus on his self and the anxiety and feelings of loss associated with it. (The disaster was the underlying feelings of loss at his father's death that were pushing for release.)

I asked if he could have thought his father's death was his fault since he had this feeling that whenever he asserted himself, it would lead to disaster, and that the father's death and the mother's depression confirmed this idea of disaster. Again a premature interpretation based on countertransference. Not that it was inaccurate, but that the patient did not yet have access to it, so it was premature.

He replied, "I don't connect emotionally, but the idea is good. I have a vivid memory of my brother's saying to me, 'Stop playing because Daddy is dead.' "

Memories of Father's Death

Second Month

The interpretation of the idealizing defense (focus on the object) and the release of some guilt over the father's death began to broach the dissociative defenses and gave the patient access to memories of and feelings about his father's death, at which point he raised the possibility of coming twice a week, with which I agreed.

"I went back to the time of my father's death and got in touch with the feelings I had before he died. How safe I felt, and he was like a god. And Mother looked up to him and he loved us. I sensed the finality of the loss. The home turned into a hell. The world changed in a day and Mother tried to keep me a baby so I wouldn't leave her. She squashed any expression of anger and she was so upset that we all became obsessed with trying to make her feel better. She would threaten to leave, saying, 'I can't take it,' and I would be terrified. I had lost my father and was driving my mother crazy. Don't grow up and leave me! That terror was my mother's idea. However, my mother got over it and I didn't. Even by the age of 6, I was quite nostalgic. I'm told my mother was sick at my birth and that I nearly killed her."

The next session began the twice-a-week schedule. Rather than produce a defensive regression, this change seemed to accommodate and foster the patient's emerging memories of the loss of his father. He began, "Last week I had a second session of my own. I went back to the day my father was killed to reconstruct it. What I remember and what I'd read. I imagined what it was like before my father died. My father's neck was broken from the impact of the crash. I kept his hat for years. His sister saw the crash. I imagined what it was like for Mother to get the news. Actually, I bolted upright in bed. I couldn't handle it. It was like it was coming at me. I felt like I was looking down the barrel of a cannon. Then I realized how Mother collapsed at the coffin, unable to look at him because he was too disfigured.

"After she got over the shock, Mother was full of hatred, both of him and of the world, and I resented her for it, but I also raged at him and the world. Mother was hospitalized for depression and had electroshock treatment. When I was in my junior year at high school at the age of 15 or 16 I was left alone in the house with my brother and sister, lonely and scared."

"From age 3 to age 21 there was so much sorrow." The patient was now sobbing. I suggested again that at the time of the loss of his father, he was also feeling destroyed by the loss of his mother. He replied, "The fear could happen anytime."

"I was 16 when I got my first job at a drugstore. I had a car accident and totaled the car. I wasn't hurt but I couldn't manage it, just like Father's death. Again I was completely guilt ridden."

(I wondered at the time, although I didn't say so, whether this had been a Russian-roulette type of accident to deal with his guilt.)

"I was a fundamentalist Christian so I had nightmares about burning in hell." The patient continued, "My mother was hospitalized two times in one year. I had thought my childhood was normal. Now for the first time, I have a sense of the arc of my life. A sense of the world before my father died. My mother's happy, my brothers and sister are happy, the world is a wonderful, inviting place."

"When I was 16, my mother was hospitalized and had ECT therapy. She wanted me to visit her at the hospital, but I went to the beach instead, and she was furious at me, accusing me of abandoning her."

Guilt About Having Killed Father Reinforces Giving Up Self

He then made a slip of the tongue: "I was killed, my father died." (He is sobbing.) "I've been waiting for it to be over ever since." He then reported a dream: "I looked in the mirror, I was old, I had gaps in my teeth like my older brother. After Father died, something horrible grew in me. Pervasive feeling of not being right."

I pointed out the slip. He had meant to say that his father was killed but said "I" instead of "Father." I related the slip to his guilt about killing his father and pointed out that this all occurred at a time very crucial for the establishment of his sense of self. He associated it with killing his father and losing his mother.

He elaborated further, "At age 12, when I was in the sixth grade, Mother had major abdominal surgery. I had a second car wreck while Mother was in the hospital. When I left home for college, she was alone. She had two coronaries in my first two years of college. In the third year, she had major abdominal surgery and almost died" (thus reinforcing the feelings of loss associated with growth and self-assertion).

"I was going with a girl in college, but I couldn't break up with her, even though I thought I should. It was spiritual homicide." I interpreted that he had associated activating himself as causing the death of his father and the loss of his mother, and to deal with guilt and loss, he had to give up his sense of self and focus on the object—his mother.

He responded, "This summer before I came here, I called my best friend to plan a visit to talk to him and get my life back on track. The night after I talked to him, he was killed in an accident and I was devastated." (As he attempts to activate himself, tragedy and loss strike again.)

At the next session, he reported feeling disappointment about the losses of recent years for the first time without self-recrimination. "Why do I have to go back to the day Father was killed? After talking to my mother on the phone, I know I have a memory of being told not to play because Father died, and the memory is totally without feeling. Mother told me what had happened. A friend of my father told my mother, who screamed 'No No' and ran outside to the yard. I realized, I remembered that moment. I reexperienced it. I was scared, the world had changed. I wanted to let it out. I was too busy, and so far had only gotten pieces of it. My mother's need to be taken care of took over and her vindictiveness when frustrated was awful."

I interpreted that to deal with this feeling of loss of both his mother and father, he had to give up focusing on himself. He responded, "I felt impotent, scared, out of it."

"I went to four funerals in the next two years. But again I wasn't feeling anything." I interpreted that it seems he had two options: to acknowledge the loss and be destroyed or to deny feelings completely.

He continued with his memories of the day his father died, saying that so much of the fear was linked to that moment. I again interpreted that he felt that the loss of both his father and mother was related to his own sense of self, and he gave it up to focus on his mother in order to relieve his fears. He responded, "Acting was the symbol of me, and when my coach left me, I couldn't handle it. I shut off my voice so I couldn't hear it anymore."

As a child, he had probably just entered a barely established oedipal phase and the loss of his father and his mother's depression caused him to regress to a closet narcissistic defensive stage, that is, to regress from the oedipal to the preoedipal.

In the next session, he reported waking with a feeling of doom, being trapped, and he related it to his present life and the inability to sell his apartment (rather than his last session). "My life is turning into Mother's. I'm getting used to expecting disaster." He then reported a dream, "I was Oswald trying to escape after assassinating Kennedy." *Free Association*: "Kennedy was killed in 1963. I was in the third grade. I was crushed by it. I'm mourning the death of the hopeful child. I was responsible for Father's death."

The oedipal theme in this dream did not became clear until much later in treatment.

I interpreted that his guilt about his father's death made him expect to be doomed, to be punished. "I'm so afraid of being punished I avoid activating myself in order to avoid it." I then interpreted that he focused on others to expiate the guilt about self-activation and death. He responded, "I dreamed that I buried myself rather than my father. I had another dream of a man holding my head under the water. I grabbed his testicles. I have other dreams about drowning, being smothered. My brother and sister holding me down. I can't breathe. The dreams trigger rage."

"Another dream, of you, me, Mother underwater. Mother is drowning and I'm able to breathe."

In the next session, he reported that his work was going better. "I'm so relieved, I'm not doomed to be punished and I don't have to go back to focusing on money. I didn't do that until I came to New York and my acting career failed." I interpreted that for him making money and losing it seemed to be experienced as surviving or being punished.

Therapeutic Alliance Established, Real Self Starts to Emerge

He then reported several recurring dreams of a positive nature for the second time epitomized by the following.

"I was back at college in my senior year. I had this old car. Afraid I couldn't start it or if I did, that I couldn't stop it. A woman spoke to me and I realized I was known there and I felt relieved."

He also had a dream about acting for the first time. (I thought that these dreams reflected the beginning of recapturing his real self as a consequence of working through some of the fear of loss in the foregoing sessions.)

Third Month

In this session, Mr. L. continued to focus on real self-activation through the medium of two dreams. In the first, he was back at college, and in the second dream, he saw his gravestone with a name on it and he was a graduate putting on a play at an alumni meeting and it was fun and he felt privileged.

Free Association: "College was the last time I was doing what I wanted to do. I started college, I majored in engineering, because this was my brother's interest, then switched to acting in the second year and 'felt golden.' Mother had encouraged me to do what I wanted since third grade. I was bored by computer courses, and with the shift to acting, I flowered, I felt wonderful, and I found a mentor to help me."

I asked whether being away from home enabled him to shift from focusing on the object to himself. He said, "Mother played the piano and was very interested in the theater. She forced my brother to take art lessons, but did not force me; however, I taught myself. But actors don't make money. I was interested in acting since elementary school. And I didn't give it up until after the failure in New York."

Rage at Abandonment by His Mother

This now led to access to his rage at abandonment. "I can remember feeling anger at Mother's terrorizing discipline. At age 9, I broke my hand by hitting the wall with my fist. I had fantasies of punching my mother's face, and I'm hurting too. Fantasies of scorching my home with a torch. My brothers would hold me down and overpower me and I would be furious. I have begun to have compassion for that kid who was having difficulty.

"I'd invent scenarios to vent my rage at Mother's attacks and Father's leaving. I hated my brother, who was self-absorbed and tried to be a father to me and I screamed at him."

Mr. L. then reported a dream: "It was my friend's funeral, but there was no casket or tears; there was much denial. The casket was in the ground for my friend and his wife, and there were kids playing around. So it was a denial that they were dead." *Free Association:* "Am I reluctant to get married because it means death?"

I interpreted that the dream expressed his feeling that self-activation leads to death, which is final. There is no repair of death. I suggested that he was afraid of a living death, which was a projection of the past into the present. (An important element here was that there was no repair to death since he had been unable to repair his feelings of loss associated with his father's death.) I added that although, in reality, the fact of death has to be faced, the feelings of loss associated with death can be repaired.

Death of the Self

This access to the anger led to dreams and memories of loss of or death of the self. "I had a dream that I was in a truck parked on a ridge that gave way and I was terrified, and I was thrown from the truck, which came down on my legs." *Free Association*: "My mother used to whip me on my legs."

"Later on in the dream, I was driving aggressively to keep up behind a school bus. The bus came at me, and backing up, I watched in horror as it squashed a 2-year-old child. The bus driver went by unknowing. My mother was horrified looking at the child. I thought I should help her, but felt partially responsible and didn't go back. I woke up in a cold sweat." *Free Association:* "I was filled with guilt and fear, it had to be me. I couldn't bear my mother's anguish."

"In another dream, I grabbed a gun from a robber and another man was shot. I was charged with the murder, but I calmly faced the charges, confident of my innocence." *Free Association:* "I was confident I could deal directly with the charges. Mother used to hit our legs with a belt. It was incredible rejection."

I again interpreted that he defended against the pain by shifting the focus from the self to the object and that he also attempted to internalize and process his mother's guilt in order to get her back. He responded: "Mother used to sing and coo to me before my father's death and she never did after that. I just had the thought that maybe that's why I sing mostly sad songs." I asked, "To soothe yourself?" He said, "I respond to soothing male voices. I'm very responsive to musical sounds. I love spirituals. They come from sadness and helplessness. I'm sad, lonely, been trying to fill that hole ever since."

"I've been looking for a dream woman to replace her. (He now briefly introduces the oedipal theme.) I have recurrent dreams of my teeth falling out or turning to jelly or of my penis falling off or swelling." I interpreted that these were expressions of the loss of the power of his self, as I was still uncertain about the role of his oedipal complex.

Memories of Mother

Fourth Month

A visit home impelled the patient to realize: "We idealized Mother. She worried us to get us to bolster her. She was a manipulative martyr. She focused on the past and she would not permit us to talk about the losses. The family had to be seen as happy." I interpreted that this denial of the loss made it impossible to repair it.

At the visit, his older sister filled in the blanks of his memory: The mother whipped only the boys, and was remorseful afterwards. She was disoriented from the moment of the father's death.

Mr. L. reported a series of dreams whose themes were of getting a second chance and coming to terms with grief and death, illustrated by a dream about his friend who had died. He told the friend he'd miss him and that he wanted to be with his friends when they grieved for him, and his friend gave a sign that it was all right with him. I interpreted that the dream expressed his ability to repair the loss. If he allowed the grief, he could move on.

This was followed again by increasing fear and depression. He was terribly drained; he had done some acting, and he said, "If I rekindle my ambitions, I'm afraid they'll be cut off by a knife. When I came here, I measured my sense of self in terms of success. So I was rejected, helpless, and devastated and had given up ambition, but I dream about acting at least 50 percent of the time, and now I'm splitting my work life between making money and developing my acting, which is what I care about."

Life never seems to cooperate with the work of therapy, for at this point, his mother was hospitalized. He visited her and talked with her about facing her death and about their lives since his father was killed. He visited his father's grave and had a flood of memories, first, third, and fifth grade. "I remember my lost, lonely childhood. I felt the responsibility for my mother. Mother has come to terms with her dying, which helped me do the same. So I could leave her and come back to New York. I didn't have two parents to support my emerging self." At this point, he is sobbing with grief.

"I flash back to my father's death. How scared, unprotected, vulnerable. I kept being flooded with feelings of loss. I told my mother about my marriage plans and reclaiming my life. Fifteen years ago was the last time I felt I was doing right. I had a dream of my tombstone with that year on it, when my hopes began to die."

At the next session, he reported, "I feel cried out. The short time at home was so intense that I'm drained, but I'm more at ease with myself." I interpreted that as he had shifted his focus from the object to himself, he seemed to feel more at ease.

"I followed my instincts or heart as I did until 15 years ago. I'm reluctant to trust it. (Having worked through some depression, feelings of loss associated with self-activation, he is now more at ease with himself.) "I seem to be able to face the depression without being destroyed. After college, my belief in my own happy ending started to die. I still doubt that I have what it takes."

I underlined that he had given up on himself and idealized the object to deal with these feelings of depression and loss and that working through the latter in treatment had enabled him to recapture his sense of self. I also pointed out that, in addition, fate seemed to have brought events involving loss to him at each developmental stage, which reinforced the childhood problem.

Self-Activation Increase Leads to Anxiety

Fifth Month

"I got more and more into my acting. Felt I was good, that I was doing the right thing. Then I had two dreams, woke in a panic, feeling I was doing the wrong thing. But during the course of the next day, what I did felt so right that it overcame the anxiety."

"I then had a dream: A baby rolled off the bed and the mother was asleep. I picked it up." *Free Association*: "I felt compassion and love plus horror for the baby. It was me. I comforted the child, wondering whether it was illegitimate. I hadn't known it was me." I interpreted that he was rescuing his real self from his mother's neglect, doing for himself what his mother had been unable to do for him.

At the next session, he reported enormous relief and feeling much better, with the resurgence of hope. But now the dread in the morning was replaced by negative feelings because he has all these "shoulds" that he's supposed to do and he attacked himself for failing them. He has also become aware that he does have another option, that he can make a living and have fun. In other words, he can activate his real self without its leading to disaster. This is a subtle, but dramatic shift.

I interpreted that the "shoulds" were the intrapsychic representations of the idealized object and focusing on them was a way of soothing and defending against focusing on himself. He said, "My work is based on 'shoulds,' not want to."

Mr. L. then reported, "Every time I focus and activate myself, the feeling is that disaster will strike and Mother will be upset. My childhood commandment was: 'Don't upset Mother, she cannot manage, you have to help her.' " I interpreted that it would seem that fate had become an ally or agent of the mother after he left home since there had been so many later-life losses.

He spoke of a feeling of guilt about "having it easy as a child." He was told he was avoiding the harshness of his father in order to have it easy, and he associated having it easy with having fun, with acting. He had felt terribly guilty about acting until he went back to the bank. Then he noted that his father had had fun, but he was killed.

Central Confusion of Childhood—Denial of Loss of Idealized Father

This led to a breakthrough into the central confusion of his childhood. "Why was Father, who was very self-activated and fun, killed and why did I have something to do with his death but didn't pay for it? I had it easy. I was responsible and guilty. I have dreams about being responsible for someone's death and not being prosecuted. Plus I have just begun to realize that I miss my father's influence.

"I was always told that if Father were alive, I wouldn't get away with this. I had a wounded mother and no father to balance it." He started to cry. "I thought that if my father were there, I'd have to toe the line. I now realize for the first time that Father might have helped. Because of the guilt about my father's death, I felt unworthy of his love, that I couldn't love him. I was so separated from Father, my feelings about my father, I had no love for him.

"I recently saw my family's home movies, which brought back my memory of Father's loving gaze. I had forgotten it. A memory of his hugging me, affectionate, but too rough. I just realized that every memory of Father was of fun. And a voice commanded, 'You can't remember that.' "

Guilt Blocks Memories of Love for the Father

"My father's family was all fun. I blocked my own love for Father because of my own guilt. It had never occurred to me. The central confusion of childhood, denial of grief for loss of my father. I thought I was still too dependent on Mother. The family implied that I was spoiled, lazy, would be rejected if Father had lived. At 7, I felt that if he had loved me before, what horrible thing had it turned into?

"This broke through into floods of memories of what it was like to be competent, whole, have fun, to rediscover love, such a sweet love we had for each other. I cried all day as if Father had just died. I mourned him this weekend, plus I also had moments of joy and peace. Feeling of being whole for the first time.

"The central trauma of my childhood, recalling the love and loss of my father. He was huge, my hero. Guilt was about killing the him in me. Couldn't remember early years when he was around and I was happy. I killed that feeling and it left an ache. I'm relieved for the first time this weekend, flooded with sweet memories of being with him.

"The horror I was afraid to confront rushing forward in fear, like holding onto a roller coaster. The reality of Father's death. That I had lost the joy, the sense of fun. I saw on the videotape my face lighting up when Father called me, it was bliss. I was more like him than the others, the apple of his eye, that's why I died. This led me to feel later with women, don't feel that sweet love or you'll lose it."

Repair of Sense of Self: The Inner Golden Core

Sixth Month

In this next session, the patient had fully recovered the positive feelings toward his father, which helped him to repair the hole in his sense of self.

"This is the first day I didn't have to cry about finding my father. I am flooded with memories. Remembering how I felt with him and he with me. We were close, not distant. He meant so much to me, and when he died, I couldn't handle the loss. I had to turn myself off and turn to my mother.

"I was so thrilled and excited by his acceptance, so identified with him. When he died, I wanted to die, didn't know what to do. Mother was overwhelmed. Watching Father taken off in a coffin, he had scared me all my life. My sister said I was very quiet and looked scared to death. Ever since that time, I have tried to fill the hole in my chest with money, with women, with acting, but I recovered enough of my relationship with him that it's covered the hole in me and I am now grateful for the little relationship I had. I realized I had been looking for him through women but it could only come from a man. It's given me a sense of peace I've never had. The world begins to look inviting again. I remembered memories of loving being with him, like magic. If Father wasn't going to tell me what to do, no one else could. At 21, I fell in love with a girl on the rebound. She rejected me. I felt so abandoned, It tore me apart, like losing my father again at 21.

"A third relationship was a reenactment of a relationship with Mother. Either reenact the relationship with Mother or with Father, as I had no self.

"Memories of my relationship with my father. My feelings glowed. I glowed with this inner golden core. Father's masculine hugs. The memories are mixed with joy. He did love me and I loved him. I feel I slew a dragon, feel whole for the first time, can see the gold in the core." (I think the patient is illustrating here how the inner sense of joy about the self comes from experience of this close relationship with the father and the loss of the father cuts off the sense of joy about the self experience.)

He continued the same theme in the next session, emphasizing how reconnecting with his father had filled the hole. He continued to dwell on memories and to mourn. "We were lost, adrift, trying to keep Mother from sinking. The last few weeks, I felt grounded for the first time, feeling the connection, not so dependent on others, or work, or women. I can feel my self-development. The connection with my father allows me to father myself."

Through a dream of his childhood friends, he remembered that all his friends had fathers who cared and led the way for them so he had to avoid them and consequently was somewhat isolated. He was so sensitive to the lack of a father that when the baseball coach rejected him, he couldn't tolerate it, gave it up, and never played again, although he was a good player.

Another dream: "Walking to the ocean, got too close, waves sucking me out took me off guard. The longer I breathed, I realized the bigger the wave would be." *Free Association:* "What's the next catastrophe? Beneath the surface we're all broken hearts."

He continued on the same theme. "I'm soaking up the memory of my father, it's food for my soul, although it's less intense. When he died, I pledged to wait for him to return. I never felt connected until I recaptured him here in the last few weeks. As a child, I felt isolated and all of my peers were jerks. I envied their families, their schools. They had structure, they had care. I lived as though I had no father with nothing to fall back on and my mother was drowning. I had killed the memory of my father and I had to hold my mother up."

He reported several dreams: one reflected anxiety about being on a journey that leads to disaster, another about connections to good friends, and then anger at God for not bringing his father back.

In the next session, through dreams of being overwhelmed and engulfed, he again goes back to himself at 3 years of age. "Calling into the black void, 'Daddy, Daddy,' being swallowed by the void. The void was caused by my mother and her depression. I did get sucked into it, like a whirlpool. Mother focused on me to suppress my anger. It infuriated me. My mother was very sick when I was born."

In another dream, he was back at college, thought he was a junior and realized he was a senior, and panicked that he had very little time left and was sad that he would be thrown back into the void again. I interpreted that he was now afraid to let go of his newly found relationship with his father.

Mr. L. responded, "I can't let go of my father yet, I just found him, it's too fast, not enough time, I'm afraid I'd lose the memory of him as I did before and realize I won't. I have recurrent dreams of being back with my old friends, a girlfriend whose family I loved. She had a wonderful father and I liked her family more than I liked her. But in the dream, she cast me out into the void. The void was hell for me. The absence of beloved father.

"I began to realize that life takes place in time, which involves change and loss. That time is eternal. I had discovered all this through my father, through dreams after the last session. I had a dream of a boy of 12, followed a rope to the end, and it was frayed. He was holding it up, smiling. He taped the end of the rope to his chest. I realized it was me in Father's garage. The boy was proud and smiling. The dream felt good. I was whole, proud and happy. The rope felt like a ribbon on my chest."

I interpreted that he had repaired the hole in his chest.

He replied, "This week I've been breaking through boundaries, finding there is nothing to be afraid of. Surprised I can do it.

"I had a fantasy that I had been swimming all this time with an anchor on my foot that weighed me down. I had to get down with it, I'm tired, to come to the surface. Felt light, I didn't have to struggle.

Thankful that I had remembered as much of him as I did. I have to have fun. It's not being irresponsible."

Further Mourning: Mother Dies

Seventh Month

Having recaptured the sense of self associated with the loss of his father, the patient returned in the next session emphasizing the contrast with his recaptured sense of self, "I realize what Father gave me. I still have trouble letting go of the memories of grief for fear I'll lose him again. Rebirth is so painful. I feel I'm developing a ground, a real self, and that facing the pain won't sweep me away as it did before. Before I never felt an underlying sense of self, whereas now I do. Growing up, I felt I had no father or a self, nothing to fall back on. Even when feeling good or doing well, the underlying threat of fear was that there was nothing there.

"I had a dream of spiders at the bottom of my coke, like ones at my father's workplace in the garage. I got sick as I was drinking it."

Free Association: "These are the remaining problems but they are not going to wipe me out. Every one of my dreams now has something to do with the theater. I think I might quit the bank to go back to acting or directing. I'm interested in the theme of breaking through despair, always wanted to say something of value, but I never before felt I had anything to say."

The patient began the next session with a dream that he was trying out for his college basketball team and asked the coach if he had a plan. The coach smiled and said he always had a plan. *Free Association*: "I felt good, that I was in good hands." (A dream of a fusion transference.)

He dreamed about the neighborhood before his father's death and it brought back feelings, thoughts about his father's beard, sensations of physical contact with his father. "I felt the top of my head coming off. I had opened Pandora's box again. Reality flooded in and blew the top of my head off. I'm frightened. Good memories trigger the pain. Sorrow is still there, but it's clear."

Another dream: "I was on a journey into a war zone. Had a helmet that would repel bullets. I thought about the moment of death. Instantly recognized, you'd realize the blow of the bullet. Would know if I were hit. Had to wait another instant to know if I'd survived."

Free Association: "I had fantasies of looking down the barrel of the gun, which was looking at Father's death and revising my own feeling of having died. The instant I went under, I never came up."

"It was so overwhelming, I turned it all off. I had another dream of burying my father's casket and then realizing I had made a mistake and I buried myself." *Free Association:* "Rebirth is so painful. The last few weeks have a sense of carrying self with me for the first time. I used to leave myself in the apartment when I went to work. I read that toughness is being who you are regardless of the circumstances and I'm beginning to feel it. I had placed my sense of self in others' opinions. By rediscovering Father, I rediscovered myself, realized I'm different from him."

In the next session, his seeing the movie "The Field of Dreams" stimulated more feelings of loss about his father. "I never played catch with him, I never told him I loved him, because he wasn't there. And I started telling him." Sobbing deeply, he said, "Bitterly I thought about Father's aspirations and his dreams. Did he fulfill himself? He seemed to have a good sense of self and was doing what he wanted. He gloried with it. He lit me up. I wanted to act, but I ended up working in a bank."

Mr. L. reported reading Robert Bly. He said, "I couldn't save my father or make my mother happy so it was a double failure. I haven't had more success in life due to my own resistance. I had to fight myself, to push myself. I thought I was lazy. Work was always making myself do it. The problem was that it wasn't for me.

"Yesterday I stayed home from work to do what I wanted, no shoulds. I wrote a letter to the parents of my friend who died. I thanked them for being family to me and told them how to handle my dead friend's children. Don't be fooled if they don't seem to mourn. As I wrote, I cried, and I began to realize that as a child I plugged into two families, my girlfriend's and this male friend's, and lost them both. I can't believe that this happened to me."

I interpreted that he had become attached to the families to try to repair the loss. "Those families were like mine was before my father died, happy and fun. Then I turned on myself and attacked myself for being pitying and complaining." I interpreted that his effort at focusing on himself and supporting himself had evoked a negative attack.

He then reported a dream, "I was closing a big door and my mother said, 'Be careful.' "

Free Association: "God was giving me permission to do what I wanted, now I was ready. There was a feeling of clarity and freedom. The universe was finally letting me follow my own path. I got an okay. God has smiled on me from within. And in daily life, I'll be enjoying myself and then the negative voices attack, telling me that I'm dumb, that I screw up, that I don't know what I'm doing. I always felt I was a preacher looking for a cause and now I'm finding it. A child's reaction to loss."

At the next session, Mr. L. reported a fantasy with his father. "I thought about my father's face, and I went into our reunion, memories kept coming up. I talked to him, saying I wanted someone to love, someone to love as much as I loved him, a woman. It was like a visit with Father, telling him what happened after he left. He cried, I fantasized lying in his arms and then I had a flash of his dead body. As long as I wasn't horrified by his death, I could hug his live body.

"As I fantasized the hug, a noise from the next apartment stopped me and I felt rage and I came back to him, told him how I missed the firm man's touch that made me feel okay. It occurred to me that I do the same thing with a little boy in our apartment house. As I talked, I became 8 to 10, felt so lost. Mother drowning. Then, he rubbed the back of my head, that's what I hungered for all those years, just that. I told him I was happy to be his son, instead of searching for someone to take his place, which I had been doing for years, and then he left."

The patient then shifted and said, "Remember the phrase from William James, 'Man should learn to trust his wants, they will lead him to fulfillment he can't see?' " He then described his readings in Robert Bly about wild men, in Joseph Campbell about "following your bliss," and then his coming upon my book *The Search for the Real Self*.

He finished with a dream: "I was saying goodbye to Sophia Loren, an adopted mother. She understood and bade me goodbye. There was a man there too. I hugged him goodbye and left."

Free Association: "I thought I was back on the day I left my mother in intensive care to die. It seemed like I was following through with myself about killing my mother."

Death of Mother Leads to Mourning, Not Dissociation:

At this crucial point in the treatment, as he continued to work through the early loss of his father and mother, his mother died in her sleep. This event challenged the momentum of treatment and how much sense of self he had recovered to deal with this latest trauma.

He reported: "I went home and grieved for her, but at the same time, I was able to have fun with the rest of my family. I feel like I've been to hell and back, but I also had a great joy. The pain on seeing her body was intense and I regretted not visiting more. I had just found my father and now I lost my mother. But after finding my father, I had this cosmic feeling that everything would be okay.

"When I got the news of my mother's death, I became extremely frightened but still stayed with my work.

"I wrote this poem: You gave it all so children would stand where you would fall. It reverberated in my mind all week. I wrote another one about coming back from heartbreak. Acts of kindness broke my heart open. The family cried and then they joked and came closer. I saw Mother's body was without her spirit, a shell.

"I woke every night in pain and cried. I was determined not to shut down this time. I was writhing like a worm stuck on a pin. All I could do was say, I'll have faith in that instant. It was all that I could take. I got through it enough to deal with the day of the funeral.

"I saw that one of my nieces was frozen like I had been and I spoke to her until she opened up."

I interpreted that he did for her what he had always wished somebody would do for him.

Eighth Month

Sublimation of Feeling About Loss of Father by Joining the Big Brothers Organization

The next session began with a dream of reunion with the father and what life had been like before he died. "It evoked a memory at age 5 at the airport with a revolving light overhead as if Father were watching over us, that he loved the airport and how exciting it was to be with Father working in the garage. The contrast after he was gone was so great and now Mother was gone too."

He was sobbing, "It's like the crying will never stop." There followed reports of dreams of tidal waves and oceans flooding the subway.

Free Association: "I will never love anyone for self again, never identify with anyone as myself again. So that if I love them and I lose them, I lose myself."

At the next session, he reported that he had joined Big Brothers. "How much I hungered for Father as a child. I can offer some of this to other kids in similar circumstances." He reported being interested in a new pastor who related to tragedy as well as to joy. It's revived his interest in religion. "It's okay to be myself, it really is all that pressure to be a star. When Father died, I thought I'd never love again; if I did, it would lead to disaster. Now I realize that the wish to love is very basic."

He then reported another dream of engulfment. "Huge waves and I had to dive under them perfectly or be crushed on the rocks. As I went in, the waters calmed. I was surprised, was I out of danger?"

Free Association: "I'm afraid to think the last wave has come." I pointed out that he seemed calm today.

"My perspective on time changed. As I grew up, I realized I was 35. I want to love a woman as much as I loved my father, but my image is of a beautiful woman with dark hair. One of my girlfriends looked like Father's family. The connection was with my father, and then she left me to marry another, one of the three biggest hurts. I was crushed. My present girlfriend is supportive, but I've held back even though I feel I love her because she doesn't fit that image of the beautiful, dark-haired woman. Also, I can't stand her mother."

Chapter Seven

Working Through Narcissistic Defenses, Abandonment Depression, and Preoedipal Conflict

The Narcissistic Defenses

After eight months of therapy, closet narcissistic defenses began to emerge.

Ninth Month

The Beautiful Woman with Dark Hair

The patient now surfaced from his mourning sufficiently to begin to explore his conflicts in relationships with women, that is, his narcissistic closet character defenses. "I wanted a dark-haired beauty. There was so much of my mother in me, I didn't have to develop it. I was in love with a woman like my mother for several years, but she attacked me and hurt me so that I stopped looking for mother types. I turned to types who were healthy and supported me. With mother types, I felt deep understanding, but I had too much trouble from them. With the healthy types, there were fewer problems, but I had a less deep understanding. I had idealized my older sister; she was beautiful. I was attracted to women early. To a woman like Father who would give me back what I lost with my father."

I said that if this were true, it was related more to his difficulty with letting go of his father than to a difficulty with women. "I never ran across the one I was looking for." I suggested that the reason for this may have been to keep the fantasy alive. He did not want a real woman who would inevitably interfere with the fantasy.

"When I think about marrying my present girlfriend, I feel I have to give up the fantasy and it tears me up. I idealize the fantasy of a woman like I did Father."

I pointed out that a real woman with real flaws frustrated this fantasy and that unattainability seemed to be a condition of the fantasy.

At the next session, he reported that an agreement to buy his apartment had fallen through, and he felt demoralized, as if his fears of doom had come true. "The harder I try, the worse it gets. I feel angry at my mother for dying and her death still hits me. I have to let myself feel the pain and not fight it."

He reported several dreams with the association that the rage about his mother's dying just led to more despair.

Rage at Mother

In the next session, the patient returned to rage at his mother for her attacks. He said his mother would lose control; the attacks would come out of the blue. "Now I am filled with anger. I feel like sometimes I'm living with a time bomb, walking on eggs. I used to put my fists through walls, broke my hand while in the fifth grade by hitting on the gym wall after the coach took me out of the game when I was doing well. What did I do to set my mother off? Why did the coach take me out? I now invent scenarios to express anger and justify self-defense. Mother couldn't stand my anger and punished me until I looked contrite. I get very angry if people aren't polite and break the rules. Once a man cut me off in traffic and I exploded in rage and told him off. I felt good afterward, not a coward, but I realized that I placed myself in extreme danger.

"I was drying my body after a shower and thought of my father's body, burned, neck broken. Just as a shell on the ground. (*The patient is sobbing.*) A jolt at remembering how much I loved Father's being alive connected with all good feelings. Maybe it wasn't so good to have a body that bad things happen to. Powerful image of Father's face looking at me, watched him from behind, being himself, such a natural being. The first girl I loved impressed me by being natural, like my father. The dark-haired girl of the dream has the same quality.

"And yet after that, a good positive memory started to come. Felt warm and good but it wouldn't come like water seeping under a door with pressure behind it. Incredibly intense and inviting, but I couldn't open the door. I tried to grasp it, but it receded, something to do with being with Father.

"As soon as I became aware, it went up in smoke. Seems like it's happening over and over again. Is there another bottom to the pain? Then I had a dream about an avalanche coming at me."

Mr. L. reported in this session, that he was doing much better with his acting. And that his girlfriend was pushing marriage and that he, for the first time, had a positive dream of marrying her.

Tenth Month

Fears of Engulfment, Abandonment by Women

This was followed at the next session by a dream in which his girl turned on him, attacked him as his mother had.

Free Association: "She's not like that. I was enraged from the dream, electric, I hit her and then felt terrible guilt." *Free Association*: "It's me who's afraid of my anger at my mother. My girlfriend never attacks me. I used to kid her about turning into a witch. I'm afraid she'll turn on me like my mother. I once punched my mother's picture until my arm hurt. The last time I saw her, I was able to keep in mind both that she loved me and hurt me."

"Mother attacked me for showing anger and I had to push it down. And I now have explosive anger and invent scenarios for rage. In the Fundamentalist Church, you were given the choice of either joining or burning. I was furious and said, 'Screw you!' "

I interpreted that his anxiety about possible marriage and involvement and commitment had turned his girlfriend into his mother, expressing his fear that he again would be stuck with the attacking woman.

He responded: "When I take a chance, I get burned, so I play it safe. I end up with women who are more afraid of being left than I am. When I go for a woman I want, I'm anxious about being attacked or abandoned. I'm worried about the hook inside me that would gut me if she left. I don't want to give anyone that power again. I feel either gutted or safe. I decided to let her move in with me."

Avoidance of Creativity of Self

Mr. L.'s acting work was now being supported by people well placed in the field. His career was opening up. He responded, "I'm scared. I realized I should have a commitment and take a risk. Brought to mind memories of the way it was before my father died. I felt a peacefulness. The loss of my father was equal to loss of a world, not the loss of a loved one. I recaptured momentarily the sense of excitement when he was alive. But nothing can change the fact that I had to grow up without him. So final. I wrote him a letter, 'I so much wanted to cry in your arms about losing you but no one did it for me.' I couldn't talk to my mother or my brother and sisters about it. Mother would break down; she couldn't handle it."

At the next session, he reported avoiding focusing on his acting to "follow out his shoulds" and avoiding his creativity. He has to force himself to work on his acting and then feels exhausted. He is overwhelmed with feelings of: "Can I do it? Will it work?" And then he reported a dream of being responsible for killing someone. I interpreted to him that his feelings of guilt about self-activation led to avoidance by the shoulds in order to soothe the feelings.

A brief visit to his relatives brought back further memories of the loss of his father, and then he became aware that when he was 7 years old, his uncle's daughter visited, and she was beautiful, the same age as his sister, who was also beautiful. On this recent trip, he had revisited that same woman, now age 48, and she had deteriorated terribly. "She brought out pictures of herself at 18 and a knife went through my heart. The first woman I ever loved, she also seemed to feel that way about me and made a fuss over me. She was like Marilyn Monroe, sexy. Her younger sister was also beautiful but a much more real person, and she also made a fuss over me.

"I recalled the excitement of being enthralled by this experience. But now she's an alcoholic and she's bloated. Perhaps she's a key to the dark-haired woman of my fantasy. I went to sleep that night feeling waves of attraction to her from the past and to the love that I experienced from her and her sister. I kept thinking, if only I open the door, she will be there, as she was when she was 18 rather than at 48."

Eleventh Month

Emergence of Wish for a Relationship Leads to Fears of Engulfment and Abandonment

Mr. L. reported feeling depressed, and getting some sense of a better life, but questioning: Is it an illusion? Having recurrent dreams about his acting, but in his daily life, he has regressed to the "shoulds." "Mother saw life as the salt mines—drudgery. I still feel unworthy of success and fun. Part of this comes from Mother's telling me that I was lazy, as well as her attitude. I am yearning to do what's right for me. I even find myself avoiding my acting."

He reported that he compromised himself in his career, that when he couldn't be successful at acting, he used money as the judge. He then reported dreams with two sets of themes. Theme one, success as an actor; theme two, "talking to a girl who went away and took a piece of me with her 'as big as a fist.' "

It brought to his mind memories of an old girlfriend and a terrific longing to see her. Then a final dream of being with a girl who made love to him. He felt enthralled, showered by the love of a beloved.

Free Association: "I got over the paralysis of myself at work and I started acting. This woman in the dream was blonde, like an old girlfriend. She gave affection with such confidence, like an older woman with a younger man. I had an older girlfriend who dumped me right after I fell in love and the loss was terrible. It was almost like the loss of my father."

As the patient activated himself more, the urge for a relationship with a woman also increased, leading to longing and a sense of loss.

He returned to the same dream in the next session: "I fantasize changing my urge for a woman into being a woman. I thought about her completeness and making myself complete. I was at a concert. It was dusk, romantic, looking for a woman. Imagining I was her. It was the opposite of my incompleteness and hollowness. However, the aching went down, and I felt a sense of peace. I imagined her saying she loved me, and I loved her, which gave me a momentary sense of completeness.

"I'm incorporating this woman who died, a beautiful dark-haired woman, to fill the emptiness and make me feel complete. This awareness decreases the ache when I usually feel it the most. I started to imagine doing what I wanted to do. Having the woman I wanted to have. This led to dreams of my brother's dying."

Free Association: "This is what my father's brother must have gone through when my father died. Maybe this is the conservative part of me dying. The antifun side."

He continued, "Then the dream changed to a black, bad guy who was escaping with me as a hostage with a gun. I wanted the police to shoot anyway."

Free Association: "I'm willing to face the painful feelings in order to get rid of the fear. We had to go into a tunnel, which looked like it was going to collapse, but then it led to an amusement area."

Final Dream: "My brother was driving me to Wall Street. A black man attacked him with a knife. The boldness of the attack was frightening. I had to face this man. I wanted to get at him no matter the risk. It reminded me of when Mother beat me, I grabbed her belt. I was angry and determined to act. I grabbed the blade of this black and then it turned out to be rubber; it was a decoy. I was afraid he would slice me to pieces with another razor."

He reported several dreams of falling in love with a woman, making love to her, and then being attacked.

Free Association: "Mother's whippings occurred if I was angry or flew off the handle. We walked on eggs around Mother, don't upset Mother, afraid to trigger a whipping if we upset her enough. She threatened to leave us."

"She said, 'Take me to the state hospital; I can't stand you people.' "

I interpreted that his brother's message seemed to be: "Where do you get off enjoying yourself when your job is to focus on Mother?"

The patient replied, "My brother's job was to keep me in mind. He was very responsible and 'should' oriented." The patient reported a dream of letting birds go free, followed by anxiety that a swarm of bees might attack them.

He again reported more self-activation, "feeling for the first time I was following my destiny, was free of the burden. Doing what I wanted rather than trying to figure out what I ought to do."

He then reported a complicated dream. "I was pursuing a beautiful dark-haired woman who felt strongly about me and I was puzzled by it and she was surrounded by disaster. Then we were both abandoned and orphaned and then an older dark-haired woman showed up and then disappeared. I realized that she was our young mother when she was beautiful.

Free Association: "As I pursued her, she turned into my sister. In other words, myself, I was searching for myself, for my own capacity, to love a woman as I loved Father."

I interpreted that this capacity had been split off and buried in order to deal with his feelings of loss of his father. He continued, "Mother turned into a wicked witch when Father died, angry, attacking. I was orphaned from both. Before, she had been wonderful and soft with me."

I interpreted again that he had to give up his focus on himself in order to support his mother.

Next Dream: "I loved this black basketball player, who cut his hand off and was giving up college just to work in a pizza place."

Free Association: "I gave up too much. My expectations for myself were too low. In the dream, he didn't want to put his hand back. He had talent. He had wonderful resources. He had effortless success. Didn't realize he had to go for it or shrink back due to sheer force, and I told him not to despair; he had to love himself as I loved him to overcome the despair of the black ghetto."

Final Dream: "The owner of a hardware store, a black man, was playing a beautiful song about loneliness. I wish I could do that. He offered to teach me. Then I was a little boy, sobbing."

Free Association: "I was that little boy who couldn't sob. Music was so sweet and pure and then I saw a black man stealing from our garage. I tried to protect myself and took a baseball bat but he took it away and beat me up."

At the next session, he reported that when his acting goes well, he has less of an ache to have a romance with a woman.

I interpreted that as he activated himself and felt complete, he didn't need a woman to complete him. He returned to the theme of the dream.

Free Association: "The black man was my deeper self. Blacks are more natural, sensual. In the first dream, the black man attacked me, then I loved the black basketball player whose hand was cut off. He had a lot of talent. He was in despair. I tried to help him. Love yourself as much as I love you and heal your heart. In the last dream in the hardware store run by the black, he tried to teach me. I thought if I could only act like that and he tried to teach me. I became a little boy in my backyard after my father's death."

Free Association: "I loved hardware. My father played a great deal with hardware, and I love black music. It's a release of deep sorrow I couldn't get access to as a child, because if I did, Mother would drown and I'd lose them both." The prior dream about the black man stealing from the garage recurred. *Free Association*: "The black boy whose hand was cut in the prior dream and the one from the garage were the same. I love the one, and he makes beautiful music, or he attacks me."

Twelfth Month

Self-Activation Leads to Depression and Reactivates Mourning

Mr. L. reported a dream of being in danger and a black man warning him so he could escape.

Free Association: "The black is a deep part of myself. I saw blacks as being real, basic, and natural. He pointed me to playing and I rediscovered the fun of playing. If I want something too much, it will be taken away. My fantasy wanting is like a knife in my gut; if I activate it too much, it will cut me. Enthusiasm leads to fear of losing. I can't get it in real life, so I focus on getting it through sex. I can't handle the tension and excitement and want to sedate myself with sex. If I don't and if I sit it out, fear spreads all over me. I just go blank."

At the next session, the patient noted that whenever he relaxed, memories of mourning came up. "I think I have it handled and then it comes back up again."

I interpreted that I thought it was more than just mourning. He was activating himself in interviews that led to recurrent images of death. This related more to his basic theme that if he activates himself, it is going to lead to doom, so that self-activation constantly reactivates and complicates the mourning process. He replied, "I had a dream about being insecure about myself in both my acting and my work in the bank. I'm still not giving the time I should to my acting. I'm splitting myself between two identities."

I interpreted he was not splitting between two identities, that he had actually made clear that he naturally belonged in acting, but his anxiety about supporting it led him to defend by pursuing the identity of a banker.

In the next session, I asked whether the reluctance to commit to his self could be related to a reluctance to let go of the fantasy of reunion with his father. He replied, "It takes courage, commitment."

Thirteenth Month

The Struggle: Overcoming the Tyranny of the False Self

Mr. L. reported, "I never found myself and let it grow. I'm now trying to face my inner self and do what I have to do. What I am, what I am to me is an actor."

I interpreted that it was so painful for him to continue and that he tended to avoid it by intellectualizing.

He replied, "I have to justify it. I was able to do my thing and it felt good and now I have shifted to the 'shoulds.' "

This was a shift from self-activation to focusing on others and following the "shoulds" and what's expected.

He then said, "Fun was associated with my father's death, too much of it was bad. I'm afraid that if I commit myself to it, I will be disappointed again."

In the next session, he talked about his difficulty in picking and choosing and accepting consequences. The more he supported himself, the tenser he got. "I realize for the first time that myself has gotten over my father's death, and now has to deal with the tyranny of the shoulds, the expectations, and the rigidity. I decided to call my false self a tyrant."

He then reported having dreams about taking his mother for a dental operation and being worried that she was dreading it.

Free Association: "I woke up with a jingle, 'Ding-dong the witch is dead, there is nothing more to dread.' I realized how a big part of my life has been dread. I dreaded going to school every morning, and I dread going to the bank every morning. I hate facing it every day. However, awareness of this seemed to lighten it. A tyrant rules by this fear."

At the next session, he continued, "Every day, I have to wrestle with the tyrant of shoulds. That they are not my purpose in life. How I try to activate myself rather than compulsively grind out the task, but I still have difficulty with priorities. What do I want to do versus what do I have to do? I'm better able to activate myself and I no longer seem to search women's faces with such hunger, but I am still too much in the shoulds."

He then made a slip, wanting to talk about failure and saying success, and his association was that success meant disappointment and failure to him. He then reported having small glimpses of being at one with himself and allowing himself to be a success. In the next session, he reported taking up meditation to help maintain access to his sense of self: "It gives me deep excitement and energy. It's almost sexual. Tapping into a positive energy within that is so deep it seems linked to the genitals. Maybe I can be who I am, but the tension is so great I release it with sexual activity. The tension comes from fear of disappointment if I do support myself. The positive energy builds up and the lid is on because of the fear of disappointment. This is the energy I felt with my father. Rather than support this energy, I drain off tension through sex and by focusing on the shoulds."

I reiterated that it seemed that it was so difficult to support himself, that the way he protected himself was through sex and the shoulds.

He externalized by saying, "I may have to quit my job at the bank to become who I am."

I replied, "If you want to be who you are, you have to be who you are."

In the next session, he reported that he had received a notice from the IRS for a tax audit that made him feel that just as he was beginning to get his act together, he had met with disaster again, but this time he replied: "If I'm going to be poor anyway, I might as well be me. It seems the more I resolve to be myself, the worse things get." He then reported a dream of his mother and his brother and his mother saying, "I like being me."

He began the next session with a dream, saying, "Facing up to my mortality decreases the illusion that I have lots of time and my worry about money goes way down. I had a dream I was trying to break into a case with something valuable and precious inside but the alarm was not turned off, so I stopped."

Free Association: "The valuable thing in the case was myself and I backed off." I pointed out that he had been late for interviews several times since the focus had shifted from others to himself.

He then reported the following dream: "I was being chased for climbing over the Gettysburg Address, which was written on the mountain like the presidents' faces on Mount Rushmore."

I interpreted that if he activated himself, he would die, like the soldiers in the Civil War preceding the Gettysburg Address.

He responded, "I realize now I have to decide what I want to do and match it with the environment, not try to get things from the environment."

Fourteenth Month

Self-Activation Leads to Death

Mr. L. was acting more, and had enjoyed some success, which was followed by depression and memories of his father's death, as he reported: "The pain of what you loved most being taken away. I had a fantasy of a devil-like creature with a hand on my heart saying, 'I got your father and I'll get you.' " In the fantasy, the creature is pulling his heart out—"He pulled out my heart and I died, but I was with my mother and father and I was happy. I realized then I had to confront the fear, the clinging."

I interpreted the feeling that if he activated himself, like his father, he would die.

In the next session, he reported, "I decided that real life's problems are not the disasters I thought."

In other words, I commented, "They are not your father's death or your death."

He continued, "Confronting my own mortality helped. I'm more peaceful, but more depressed, but I'm off the shoulds treadmill and doing more of what I want to do. There is such physical tension in my shoulders and back and neck. I'm bracing myself against the next blow. He reported starting to work with the Big Brothers and also volunteering to teach English to foreigners through the church. He then returned to the difficulties he was having sticking with his acting: "I lack the strength to keep myself at it."

I again wondered why he continued to avoid it.

At the next session, he reported a reunion dream about his father and also making love to a dark-haired, beautiful woman, both as defenses against self-activation described in the prior session. He then reported: "I was working at my acting and had a fantasy of being killed in an auto accident."

I reinterpreted, "If you activate yourself, you will die like your father died." This released another tide of self-activation and in the next session he reported a dream: "A high-school teacher who was positive to me. Hadn't thought about him in years. He was happy doing what he wanted. Realized he was one of the few caring men in my childhood. I told him I was doing okay. Then I had sex with Madonna and it felt so good and then I was in my surfing wet suit, which I wore at 17. Felt exalted, attractive. So good about my body. Cherishing pride in my body. The way I used to feel about the beautiful women, I felt about my own body. The dark-haired, beautiful woman has moved into me. The sense of tenderness and appreciation I always looked for in and from a woman was now present in me."

I suggested that he had regained a very important piece of his sense of self. He replied, "But it was not narcissistic. I woke up thinking about a song that went, 'Don't sell yourself short.' "

This led to the working through, in the next two sessions, of extensive memories of crucial times in which, "I felt I was becoming myself, but which were followed by disaster." He recalled that the first time was his father's death. The second was between the ages of 15 and 16 when he had a run-in with the police, who found him necking with a girl in his car and reprimanded him. He wrecked the car, and then had another run-in with the police, was cut from the basketball team, and his mother was admitted to a psychiatric hospital. All this occurred between ages 15 and 16. Then between 21 and 22, his mother received surgery for cancer; he broke up with a girlfriend whom he had outgrown, fell in love with another, who jilted him. When he was 23, he moved to New York, and his mentor lost interest in his acting career.

From age 25 to 33, he did well in his banking job, had a lot of money, was acting, had a good relationship with a woman, and at age 33, he moved to a new apartment. The woman dropped him. He broke up with his partner in business, and then the business went bad. The apartment building cooperative defaulted. The bank defaulted on the co-op and his friend was killed, and he lost a great deal of money in an investment. Recently, however, he said in treatment that there was an undercurrent of rising progress that was taking over from the disaster.

I interpreted, "There seemed to be a litany of external disasters that reinforced the inner feeling that if you self-activate, you will die."

The fact that the interpretation was integrated was revealed in the next session. He began with a recurrent dream, "I had a phone call that my last uncle had died."

Free Association: "If I self-activate, I will die. This uncle was the closest to a father I ever had. Spent summers with him and was close to him and he now has died." This was followed by a dream of "learning how to die so I could live." In the third dream, "I was with a police officer who saw how anxious I was and said I should get straight what I was fearing. That I was fearing the wrong things."

Free Association: "That morning after the dream, I felt fearful and had an anxiety attack. I remembered how I was in the third grade, and I tried to soothe that little boy in myself. All I wanted to do was put my head on someone's chest and cry. I had no one I could do that with. I felt it, and I comforted myself. A real change—before, I could find no comfort. Finding a place inside that's warm and safe. I never had that before. After that last interview, I felt so light. I felt that I had lifted such a burden. It felt like a beautiful way of being—relaxed, calm. One of the most beautiful moments in recent years."

I pointed out that he allowed himself to be himself without the fear of dying.

He then shifted to talking about his relationship with his live-in girlfriend, who wanted to marry, but he was reluctant, "It's not that I am so reluctant to marry her. If I can complete myself, I won't have to look to the picture-perfect ideal woman to do it, and then I can marry her. We have been together for five years. I realize it is unfair to her. I'm still frightened to close off other alternatives."

I interpreted that commitment to his self meant commitment both to his acting and to a woman—all of which seemed to be equated with death, which is why he feels the need to avoid it.

Fifteenth Month

Self-Activation Leads to Death and Conflict Over Marriage

Mr. L. reported that he had decided to stay home and do what he wanted and had a wonderful time with "no shoulds." The next night, he had a dream of his brother killing his wife. "I was horrified. I tried to help him cover it up. We both were arrested. I talked to the authorities, trying to cover our guilt, and I said to them, 'If you're not going to let him go, at least let me go.' "

Free Association: "Guilt about murder and my brother and the cover-up had led to thoughts about my girlfriend: the conflict of wanting to be with her and also wanting to be free."

He continued, "My girlfriend had to decide on a job that might take her out of town, so that we have to decide whether or not to stay together. I had a fantasy of letting go of Mother's suffering. Not having to focus on Mother and her pain, which I had to process for her. I told myself that she was dead and it didn't matter anymore."

I interpreted that I thought from the fantasy that the dream was of his killing his mother by activating himself.

He said, "I think that's right, because the guilt feels more like matricide." He then reported, the next day, a dream of a wonderful trip to Antarctica, the awesome beauty of the scenery, on a trip with his girlfriend, but he got attached to another woman."

This led to a discussion of his conflict with women. "I thought of myself as fickle."

I pointed out the paradox that with his girlfriend, the affection is good, the sex is good, she supports him, doesn't allow him to dump on her, but he's still looking for another woman.

He questioned, "Why am I still so attached to the package? What I am attracted to is the perfect woman, who makes me look better in other people's eyes. She has to be soft featured and have a soothing voice, the way my mother was before my father died. My girlfriend's features are sharper and her voice is less soothing. Maybe I am trying to recapture the mother I lost when my father died, or could it be that I'm not honoring my own life? I am unable to commit to myself, so I can't commit to her."

I reinforced the paradox that since sex, affection, and mutual self-support are there, what else could he be looking for?

Mr. L. was 36 today. His girlfriend, in a deep discussion, decided to take a job in New York to be with him, felt his withholding on commitment, emphasized her wish to be married, and he reluctantly backed into agreeing to plan marriage in the spring or summer. This was followed by several dreams recapturing his mother's disapproval of his emerging sexuality in adolescence and his mother's coming into the room when he was making love.

Free Association: "She's furious at me. I confronted her and said I was a man and needed sex and would have to move out." He then meets a friend who is crazy about his own girlfriend and asks him, "How do you decide to marry?"

In another dream, he sees his mother in her casket and has to bury her. From his free association, what emerges is the fear that marriage will cut off sex with others or even cut off sexual passion in the marriage. His fear is that if he commits to himself and to her in this way, his mother will die. He is quite depressed and talks about feeling old: "Where did the time go? In adolescence, my sexuality upset my mother a good deal and it wasn't until I came to New York that I had free rein, but whenever I fell in love, the relationship ended. Here I am, 36 and both in career and in relationships a failure—I'm not what I want to be."

Sixteenth Month

Consolidation of Self and Investigation of Defensive Reunion with a Beautiful Woman

"When my last uncle, my father's brother, died, it dredged up all my feelings about my father's death. This uncle had been the only male model for me after Father's death. He bought me a pony, took me fishing, taught me how to shoot a gun. The closest man to me after my father died. I realized I never got over wanting my father back. I got a clear picture of how my life was with my father and without him. The thought of having my father back was so sweet that I couldn't bear to think about it. I was so complete with him and incomplete without him. I began to imagine I had him back. Somehow I regained the world I lost. The aching insecurity disappeared. I imagined myself growing up with him, and then realized he might have been proud of me. That had never crossed my mind before.

"I regained him and the world and part of myself that I had lost. The world let up and became magical, full of promise. I said to myself, 'Don't forget to enjoy the magic of being alive.' "

At the next session, Mr. L. consolidated his recapture of his sense of self and became aware that despite the fact that he recaptured it, he had not yet committed himself to it: "I had this feeling that Father was with me all the time. I'm getting the security I have never had. I thought the world was good. I regained my past self that was missing. I began to have a sense that tragedy happens, but it's not punishment or due to me. I'm not being singled out. I feel now in company with others as far as tragedy is concerned. However, I always feel a step behind in my life although I keep very busy."

I interpreted that it seemed that he was avoiding throwing himself into a full commitment to himself in his acting, in his relationship with his girlfriend, and in life in general.

In the next session, he began to investigate his relationships with women further: "I remember two women who rejected me just as I committed myself to them. There is something in me that says, 'Don't you dare care, you know what happens.' "

I interpreted that the fact that he cared seemed automatically to mean disaster.

He replied, "I was surprised to find that I felt responsible for my father's death. My mother was always asking me, 'What did you do?' As if I had done something wrong. When I open myself up to women, I think they see the monster I am and run away."

I interpreted his feeling that he was responsible not only for his father's death, but also for his mother's turning away after his father's death.

He replied, "What did I do to turn her away?"

He then reported a dream of being associated with the murder of a woman found dead in the trunk of his car, for which he felt severe guilt. Another dream was of his brother's killing his wife, and he was trying to help him, but also get himself out of it. And a dream of a high-school friend killing his girlfriend.

I interpreted that it would appear from his dreams that he feels that there is something lethal about himself.

He replied, "I'm a Scorpio and my sting kills. In college, I read a novel based on Cain and Abel and looked in the mirror to see if the sign of Cain was on me."

In the next session, he reported another dream: "I'm in a building with a woman, an old flame. The building starts to fall and I am caught, trapped, and crushed to death."

Free Association: "I try, I'm so busy, I can't get everything done. I don't seem to have the push or the courage to follow through. In the dream, I try to hold the building up."

I interpreted that if he commits to himself fully, he will have to let go of his fantasy about his father and die.

He responded: "I am vacillating over quitting my bank job. I'm crushed by trying to hold the job and also do what I want to do, and yet I can't quit the job until I sell the apartment."

Then he reported thoughts about feeling how lonely his aunt must be without her husband, and this made him turn more toward thinking that he loved his girlfriend.

I interpreted that he was projecting his loneliness onto his aunt; that is, if he commits to himself, he will be without a family and then cling to his girlfriend as a family, not as a wife.

He asked, "Does committing to a woman give meaning to life?"

I responded, "No, commitment to self precedes commitment to a woman."

This material led to beginning insight into the dynamics of his fantasy of the beautiful dark-haired woman. He said, "In my 20s, I chased women. I was predatory for sex, not a relationship. I had an inner hunger. This morning, I realized that I wanted my father—I couldn't have him—I wanted my mother the way she had been, and couldn't have that. I wasn't able to do my acting. A relationship with a beautiful idealized woman was the only possibility."

I added, "For hope!"

He replied, "Marrying my girlfriend would be giving up that fantasy."

I again interpreted that the fantasy was a defense against his feeling of hopelessness.

He began to tear and asked, "How much of the world do you create and how much do you accept?"

I replied that in his relationship with his girlfriend, he seemed to be able to have his cake and eat it too. He has the relationship, he doesn't have to marry her, or fully commit himself to her, which allows him also to hold on to the fantasy of the beautiful idealized woman, which is a reunion fantasy with his family, and that commitment to himself, whether it's in acting, with a woman, or in treatment, means death, loneliness, and giving up the family. So he protects himself by holding back, and investing in the reunion fantasy.

He began to cry, and he said, "I think an awful lot about death."

In these four sessions, he had moved from consolidating the inner sense of self to the problems involved in activating that sense of self in work and relationships and treatment, that is, he's feeling that to do so is to court death.

In the next session, he investigated further the beautiful dark-haired woman fantasy as a condensed family fantasy. He began with a dream: "I was flying with my boss, the wind was whipping, we were trying to land. I was afraid we were going to crash."

Free Association: "It was very risky."

I interpreted that, in light of the last session, if he committed himself to himself, he would die, like his father had.

He replied, "That's why I clung to the condensed fantasy of a beautiful dark-haired woman; it was Father's family. The first girl reminded me of his family, with her, I was recapturing part of him and my mother as I wanted her to be. It was a completion of myself. When I woke up this morning, I thought this must be what it feels like to feel normal, there is no dread. The condensed fantasy has lost some of its power. I don't feel the yearning and the need to search for her. It was diminished. I see women more realistically, as they are. Then my girlfriend looks terrific."

I interpreted how the reality of a woman replaced his condensed fantasy. He said, "The thought of marrying her was not so frightening and I didn't swing back to the fantasy woman."

This movement in the next session again led to defense. He presented a dream: "My uncle was dying of cancer. At a family conference, we decided that his wife should poison him to keep him from suffering. He ate the poison and died, and we all felt incredible remorse. We buried him in the front yard. A big machine dug up the casket and then held it up in the air."

Free Association: "Horrible. Guilt ridden. We made the wrong decision. Irrevocable. He was the closest friend to my father and to me. I feel a responsibility and a guilt about Father's death and killing my own real self."

I interpreted that letting go of his father is killing him, so he is preserved through the beautiful-woman fantasy, and as he overcomes that, the guilt about his father surfaces and he has to punish himself.

He replied, "Last year, I tried to give my father up and my mother died and that threw me back into being afraid of losing Father. Then I realized I had three levels of this: (1) a fear of losing my father, (2) a guilt about killing him, and (3) a fear of my own death."

He then reported another dream, which revealed a further level of this complex problem: "I was making love to a girl and she wasn't interested. I realized that all I had to do was leave her alone and walk out to the sunlight. Why was I working on it so hard? I didn't have to do that. Just to be happy."

Free Association: "The feeling is that I don't want to do it."

I interpreted that this was a negative transference dream about focusing on himself, committing himself to the work in the sessions.

He responded: "I'm afraid of wanting anything too much, as if there's a knife attached to it. The desire to have my father back was the most pressing desire of childhood, and the thought of it ripped me up. It became associated with any strong desires bringing pain."

This clarification of transference led to another dramatic dream about his friend who had been killed: "He was in my apartment and it was unclear whether he really was there or he was gone. It was an illusion. Then he appeared to me alone and I touched his arm. I was so grateful and happy to have him back. I kissed him. I told him I loved him, and then he disappeared, and then I went to a party and I chased this dark-haired beautiful woman, and as I did so, she turned into a dog as I was trying to kiss her and pat her and she growled at me. I realized it was not her but a dog, and that it was very dangerous to treat her as a woman."

Free Association: "My family and her family denied my father's death and the dream is a reunion with my father and part of myself through the beautiful-woman fantasy."

The patient was 15 minutes late for the last session, at which he announced that he had not told me before, but he was going on Christmas vacation for two weeks. I attempted to use this to point out the unconscious resistance to the level of the work, but without much success, and he left for a two-week vacation.

Seventeenth Month

Working Through the Affect Underlying the Fusion with the Object Defense

Mr. L. returned from his vacation, announcing that he had asked his girlfriend to marry him and that she had agreed. He felt that he couldn't come back to New York and continue the ambivalence. He had to act. And then he worried, "Was I giving up a dream?"

I asked: "Were you giving up a real dream or a protective defensive fantasy?" I again asked why he hadn't told me about his vacation, but he responded that it probably was because he had been too pressed and too busy.

In the next session, he spoke of more self-activation. He's doing better at the bank and his acting is going extremely well. Then he reported a dream: "I was in the ocean, a fog. The water was whirling and threatening. I saw a woman in the water and jumped in and kissed her. I said, 'Drown with me.' "

Free Association: "It was like meeting my other half, completing me. I'm tired of struggling with this. It's complete self-absorption and it's an infantile attitude."

I interpreted that if he fuses with the woman, then the struggle is over.

He responded: "It was like incredible sex. It sucks you in and you're gone."

I interpreted that it was a way of giving up self and fusing with the object, a protection against self-activation, a repetition of what happened with his mother, shifting the focus from himself to the object. He then reported a sequence of dreams. First, he recaptured his sense of boyhood adventure and then had a flood of sadness, over his mother; second, a dream of soldiers trapped in the Normandy surf and unable to get to shore; and finally, a dream of being accused of trying to engineer his mother's death. He woke feeling shocked, appalled, insulted.

Free Association: "I'm killing my mother by focusing on myself. I had an old dream about being in my office planning a dinner party. I was talking to a guest. I was in a fog. And then I was back home with a pretty young girl. I loved her and felt connected to her."

Free Association: "I woke up sad that Mother never knew who I was.

I never knew who I was—or who she was, because of my infantile view. I'm starting to see the effects of my focusing on her."

He then reported another dream: "I was aching at the loss of Mother's early life, not my own."

I interpreted this as his wish to fuse with his mother to repair the loss of his father.

Free Association: "Father's death ruined my mother's life, and mine, too. I dreamed of a beautiful dark-haired woman as a reunion with my mother." There followed another dream: "I'm riding a motorcycle through water. I realized it was gas, and could explode any minute and kill me."

I interpreted that if he activated himself and didn't fuse with his mother in the dream, he would die.

He responded: "I'm feeling more sense of entitlement. I'm feeling more positive with my fiancée. I'm starting to—I'm thinking of changing my job and working more on my acting."

In the next interview, the same theme was expressed in dreams that if he activated himself, he would then seek a woman with whom to fuse. I interpreted that self-activation frustrates the fusion with his father and mother, exposes him to feelings of loss. He feels the loss of his father and seeks reunion with his mother. I point out that self-activation separates the real self from the grandiose fused defensive self. When his father died, he had a fused image of him, then with his mother, and then with women to deal with the loss, and he was teasing out these defenses here.

He then reported a dream of being attacked by a man and beating him up.

Free Association: "I was fed up and I was sad, however, I had to kill him. He asked, 'Is it me attacking and killing or is it you?' "

He had a final dream: "I finished my tasks. I wanted to enjoy living and a party. There was no one there."

Free Association: "Every time I experience the joy of living, it is crushed by the feeling of loss."

At the last session of the month, he began with a dream: "I had to shoot a dog and move on, and then I dreamed that I was free, had a fresh start and renewed and thought about going to graduate school, but I had to serve time in jail first, which was inside my father's tool shed. I played the song 'Bridge Over Troubled Waters.' I felt I had a bridge over troubled feelings. I left and thanked my jailer for a time of peace and growing."

Free Association: "I think the jailer was either you or my father and mother. I found a tree with a hole at its core with a box in the middle put there by my father. The tree asked me to remove the box so I could grow. The tree was me."

Eighteenth Month

Continued Struggle with Defenses Against Pathological Affects Evoked by Self-Activation

In the first session of the month, Mr. L.'s real self-activation was portrayed in two dreams: In the first dream, he is landing a jet on an interstate highway, and in the second dream, he is getting a big break in a play. In the first dream, the feeling is that it's terribly dangerous to land this jet, as something bad might happen. And in the second dream, his acting in the play leads to the cast's being embarrassed and he feels mortified and ashamed.

Free Association: "It was the real me. I felt ashamed, but at least I had been myself. Even though I felt ashamed, I'm glad I did it. I stood up for myself. Before, I wouldn't have done it. Occasionally, I have thoughts about stopping treatment."

Predictably, in the next session, he retreated to further defense. He began: "I used to feel that if I supported myself, I would go into a black hole. I now feel I can endure the suffering and hold onto myself, but I still feel it will not turn out okay."

Then he moved into defense; "I had a dream about a big, friendly dog who wants to come into the house, but I can't let him in, because it's not my house."

Free Association: "It's my real self."

He then reported a second dream of having sex with a woman while her husband watched, enjoying it, which led to free associations that his sexual hunger is so great that he debases himself to get it. He uses sex to fill the hole of trying to be himself. "At least in sex, I feel I am real. But then I'll feel I'll be rejected and the sex will lead to disaster."

I interpreted that he's better able to express his real self in sexual life and in his work, but also here it triggers feelings of disaster.

Free Association: "I was always good at sexual games with women.

It felt right and natural. It makes it harder for me to give up seeking other women. My interest in acting used to be natural. I used to enjoy doing it, but now there's all this tension."

This led to a dream: "Mother was dead. I kissed her goodbye. I felt that I had to go through those awful feelings again and then realized I didn't. I braced myself for those feelings and they didn't come. And then I bought a grand mansion and I loved it for the ego gratification, but hated the work."

Free Association: "It looks like I have gotten a hold on my feelings about my mother's death and the rest of the dream is substituting grandiosity for expressing my real self. Am I going to continue as a banker or am I going to pursue an acting career?"

This theme continued in the next session, where he reported a dream about being very creative and doing what he wanted to do, followed by a dream of monsters and death. He talked about being tempted back into banking to avoid the tension associated with acting. And that more and more, banking seems real, whereas acting seems like a fantasy. And he's not sure it's for him.

I asked, "What can you do to test out this conflict, whether or not it's for you."

His answer was: "To get more into acting."

He then watched a videotape of his mother at age 76 telling her sister, "I want to tell you of my wants and dreams."

"It made me feel the futility of my own wants and dreams, the death and aloneness. Mother's love for us kept her going so we weren't just a burden to her."

At the same time the patient talked about having decided to become a Big Brother to an 11-year-old boy, which is helping him to sublimate his feelings about fathering his deprived self. At the end of the session, he reported feeling better, rediscovering hope.

At the next session, he turned his focus to relationships: "I'm shocked at the idea of marriage, and as I feel that way, my fantasy of the woman of my dreams returns. I feel as if that 3-year-old is coming back. I'm scared of marriage and of commitment, that I will be gutted as I was when my father died."

He then reported a dream, which was the second of a series of dreams about airplanes. A plane is landing, there is a fear of its crashing or killing people, but the pilot is calm and nothing happens, and he is relieved.

Free Association: "I could cause disasters by activating myself."

I interpreted that if he activated himself, he felt that he would kill people.

He then reported a second dream: "I'm playing shortstop at second base in the game, but it's the wrong position."

Free Association: "The kind of acting I'm doing is really not for myself; it's for others."

Another dream: "A beautiful dark-haired woman was getting old. I had to take her home."

Free Association: "My preoccupation with this woman is beginning to fade. I used to use women as a way of feeling good about myself. I think I pursued money and success in order to get the perfect woman. I've been looking for an external key when I should have been looking inside. Sex was the game and I was good at it. The game gave hope, but the hope was based on a fantasy of a false self and depression lies beneath it. Can I turn the focus on myself to fill the hole?"

I interpreted in this session his need to focus on women as a way of regulating his feelings about himself and dealing with the feelings of disaster and loss. This brought him back, in the next session, to focusing on himself with a dream as a child of seeking out a minister to help him deal with the feeling of devastation. And then he remembered that at age 7, after his father died, they moved away from their neighborhood, which was another devastation.

He recalled, "My father's not coming back, what do I do with this ache? Then I felt guilt."

I interpreted that the guilt was caused by his focusing on himself.

He replied, "I have no father. How will I become a self? But in my everyday life, I am beginning to reassert a feeling of entitlement to focus on myself. In other words, I'm staying at home to do some of my acting work and to do what I want."

In the next session the patient talked about how he was better able to focus on himself and support it rather than retreat to fantasies about women. He then would begin to feel separation dread and defended either by avoidance through seeking instant gratification or directing his behavior to what he should do, rather than what he wanted to do.

He said, "I've been supporting myself, but in the shower, I felt a dread, and with the dread, I felt a pull to go for immediate gratification. The future to me is filled with depression and death, so I should get my gratification now. There's a feeling of loss of hope and faith with no reason to endure and stick it out."

I interpreted that faced with the issue of activating himself, he sees death, and then he protects himself by seeking immediate pleasure or following shoulds rather than wants.

He replied, "Events reinforce the shoulds."

He then spoke of the enormous anxiety and tension associated with self-activation.

"It brought up memories of my mother's attacking me with a belt, the feeling of the need to be loved by my mother and being attacked instead. My world view is related to that. Religion reinforced it. I lost my father and I had a battling mother, which buried myself more deeply."

He then reported a dream: "I was surrounded by polar bears. I could fly away if I had confidence, but I lost confidence and would drown or be eaten. The bear was in the home like my mother, marauding in the house. I jumped in the car, rolled up the windows, and escaped."

Free Association: "It's the terror I felt when Mother was on a rampage. Something in me was dying, my sense of self. Mother couldn't allow expressions of anger, because she was so angry. I suppressed it. Anger was bad. I couldn't have my own indignation. Father's death gutted me and Mother's attacks stripped me again. If I expressed any anger, she would die."

In the last session of the month, he reported a dream that expressed his increasing confidence and self-activation: "I had this dream of making progress in treatment. Then I was in an elevator, and the elevator was in free-fall, but rather than crashing, at the last minute, the brakes came on."

Free Association: "The key is to face the terror of Mother's attacks. I need courage to face them."

He then reported a second dream: "A plane that I thought might crash landed, and I got off. I did what I wanted to do. And then I had a second dream of testifying on a radio program on psychology. And then when I was clearing out the garage, I became a cleaner."

Free Association: "This represents the shoulds in order to avoid self-activation. I woke up this morning refreshed, the universe seemed friendly and weight was lifted. I was able to stay more with self-activation, not so much under the weight of the shoulds. Myself is still immature and needs support and encouragement, but I now feel it will work rather than that it will die."

Chapter Eight

Working Through Neurotic Defenses and Oedipal Conflict

By the 18th month of therapy, interpretation led Mr. L. to the early special narcissistic relationship with his mother before his father died.

Eighteenth Month

In the first two sessions, Mr. L. reported feeling depressed, afraid to move, waiting for the next disaster to strike, and procrastinating with self-activation by being preoccupied with his banking work.

At the end of the week, his girlfriend went away for two weeks, which led to the following dream: "I dreamed of the agony over the breakup with my first girlfriend when I outgrew her. I felt I was betraying her. I was locked in by awesome guilt and felt that she wouldn't survive."

Free Association: "It's about the guilt and responsibility I feel for women, for the woman's happiness, just like with my mother. While my girlfriend was away, I again started to look to other women for a fling, to play the game, to get ego support."

I interpreted the dream as a response to a combination of his efforts at self-activation in treatment and his girlfriend's going away, that the efforts at self-activation brought on a feeling of betrayal and loss of his mother. If he activated himself, he would betray his mother, lose her support, and lose his grandiose self. I pointed out how he seemed to work hard on all his other defenses, but with this issue he seemed to tread water; that is, he continued to avoid full self-activation.

This pursuit of the continued need for defense against self-activation led to a dramatic change and deepening of the focus on the earlier relationship with his mother in the next session, where he reported early memories of being dressed by her, playing with her, getting away with things, and having a special relationship with her; everything was okay as long as she wasn't angry.

I asked, "Could your mother have promoted a special relationship that felt good, except when you were angry or said No to her or she said No to you, thus frustrating the relationship? You learned to play the game with women long before the death of your father, and have always played it well with women."

He responded that his girlfriend was different. She didn't make him responsible for her happiness. The woman he dreamed about had made him responsible and she attacked him if he wasn't.

He continued, "My mother had been very sick when I was born, had a hysterectomy right afterward. She always introduced me as her baby and I never objected. Father would have helped me out of that if he'd lived. Maybe Father loved me in a healthier way. (His father supported his real self.) My mother also was called a baby by her father and she was pampered by her father like she pampered me."

I then took two weeks' vacation. The deepening of the work was indicated by the fact that when I returned, the patient continued at the same level.

He began. "Since the last session, the sense of dread has gone. I began to think more about what occurred before my father died. I was the last child. I had been a difficult birth, so Mother had a special relationship with me. I was smothered by being her baby, performing for her. My sisters—I also performed for them. But my being independent was not acceptable to my mother, and I'm even more certain of that after Father's death, but it was probably there before.

"When I tried to move out with my brothers, I was called very spoiled and attacked, so I regressed back to her. I looked for my father to help me. I didn't have to be special with him. I didn't have to play Mother's game. I was able to be myself. Probably that's why I looked to him so longingly, to deliver me from Mother's smothering, and I lost my savior and Mother was drowning in depression, and I regressed to her in spades. But I had self-loathing for my playing the game. I understood that I needed Mother's approval and I took responsibility for it. If I took responsibility, I thought I could have stopped it then. It gives me that power to do it now. Now I don't want to be special."

I asked whether the game playing that he did with his mother occurred in his relationship with me, pointing out that he had no complaints about me.

He replied, "I don't see it." I asked whether he might be idealizing me as the father who helped get him out of the bind with the mother. I was concerned that unacknowledged transference might block deeper investigation of the earlier relationship with his mother.

He replied, "I have to guard against making you a father figure. So I don't ask for much. I have to do it myself. I allow you to make observations."

I interpreted that in childhood, his real self led to his mother's disapproval and the loss of his father, so perhaps he can't allow himself to rely on me and has to handle me with kid gloves.

He replied, "It's too dangerous for me to be myself."

In the next session, he reported that he had felt depressed after the last session, then began to feel good, with a resurgence of hope. He realized how dangerous it was to be himself.

Transference Interpretation

I interpreted that it was dangerous to be himself with me, that the emphasis he placed on self-activation in the sessions might actually be a kind of game similar to that he played with his mother, in order to please me rather than to express himself to deal with his feeling that if he does focus on himself, there will be nobody there to respond. He had to take care of himself; there was no one else there. He could not experiment and test his self in a relationship in which he had to be responsible for protecting his self and his mother against death.

He replied, "I either have been drawn to things or whip myself to do them. I can't whip myself anymore."

I interpreted that perhaps the lash of focusing on the object still operated here with me.

He replied, "I viewed life as a drudgery, all the same with no hope. I don't know what to do."

In the last session of the month, the interpretation spurred greater self-activation. He reported: "I was more myself but I have to be superalert to stave off disaster and not get smashed. I can't just live. I had a dream of being excited, the whole world looking sunny, seeing my mother, being happy, being a good actor, resurgence of hope. Then I dreamed that a friend attacked me and there was another disaster, and I began to feel guilty about women and I remembered when things were so bad with my mother. I can't seem to just live."

Nineteenth Month

Focus on Self-Relationship with the Mother Before the Father's Death

Interpretation of the transference leads to fear, sex, and guilt, which leads to oedipal conflict, not sexual abuse.

Mr. L. again reported doing more of what he wanted to do and then dreaming about disaster. I interpreted that his difficulty with self-activation clearly preceded his father's death and was internalized so that it was inside his head before he had lost his father.

This led him to review and remember how he had lost his mentor after he started his acting career, which reinforced his feelings of the loss of his father and mother.

He said, "I felt devastated, I never contacted him again. I decided to give up acting, which led to disaster, and to make a lot of money and go back when I had enough money." He would defend against his fear of disaster by having money.

In the next session, he reported overcoming the feeling of its being a capital crime to hurt a woman. He talked about his sister, who confirmed the game that went on between him and his mother, and then he talked about how the distractions, that is, the "shoulds," pulled him away from doing what he wanted to do. He then missed the next interview because of a trip, was supposed to call me, but forgot. I suspected that he forgot because of guilt about avoiding treatment.

He replied, "I don't know, I was very busy, and I let it go at that level."

He continued, "If I did what I wanted as a child, I felt guilty, I felt it would start Mother into the death spiral. What have I done? Action is doing something bad, Mother's death spiral. It was related to the time of Father's death."

I disagreed and said I thought that it was earlier, at his mother's withdrawal when he activated himself and was dramatically reinforced at his father's death with his mother's falling apart, and that he had a need to avoid the earlier withdrawal.

He replied, "I spent my life trying to avoid trauma, Father's death, Mother's death spiral. Mother cooed with me, as well as attacked, and was seductive."

I interpreted that he had internalized the feeling that if he activated himself with his mother, he'd be abandoned, and his father had been a buffer against this feeling.

He replied, "I see it's in me, but what do I do?" I asked, "Why do you feel helpless?"

At the next session, he again talked about trying to figure out what he wanted and again at having dreams of attacking himself.

I pointed out that it seemed to me that he had no difficulty knowing what he wanted to do. The difficulty was dealing with the feelings of loss that it brought up.

He began to sob, talking about how much he wanted to do but how much trouble he had doing it, but this now led to the first opening, to the oedipal conflict: He reported a very early memory of playing in the backyard, and he didn't know why, but he felt scared: "Something scared me."

Transition from Preoedipal to Oedipal

Exploration of his earlier narcissistic relationship with his mother led to the memory of playing in the backyard and feeling very scared. Something scared him. This brought to the patient's mind the feeling that he was afraid of being out of control, of being violated. "It makes me think of sexual abuse. It wasn't just my mother's temper." This led to another dream, "taking gobs of mucus out of my mouth." *Free Association*: "Could someone have ejaculated in my mouth?" This leads to feelings of fear. "I can't believe this happened."

This fear then led to memories of his uncle, who had come to visit them right after his father's death: "I can't believe this happened. Could he have abused me? Then I had the second revolting thought. Could Mother have had sex with him in her grief or drug-induced stupor? Could I have heard it in the next room?

Something must have happened then. Trying to remember brings up fear, a swirl of feelings of guilt, sex, death. "I'm drowning in guilt, the finality of death."

"I might have been willing to do anything to get my father back. Did I have ideas of getting rid of my father in order to have my mother to myself." (This was the patient's first mention of the oedipal conflict.)

He then followed with a dream: "A naked woman is walking with a naked youth. I run through the woods. An older man with a dachshund comes after me. I stop the dog with my foot, and try to soothe him. This big athletic guy attacks me and I fend him off. I'm ready to poke his eyes out. How dare he try to intimidate me in my own neighborhood? I woke up crying and frightened."

Free Association: "Could the dachshund be a penis symbol? I thought of a tank in my father's yard that had a big nozzle, my father's big penis, and then a movie. 'The Drifters,' where the mother tries to seduce the son. It brings on fear. Angelica Houston in a slip reminded me of my mother, ugly, frightened. Mother had an ECT when I was 8 years old and again when I was 16. When she was pregnant with me, she almost died of uremia. One year later, she had a hysterectomy. She had major surgery when I was 12. Mother went from sobbing to vengeful anger at the boys."

This ended the interview. He had introduced the oedipal conflict, but more or less stopped at the surface.

In the next session, the patient began with. "It was my feeling of fear that led to the idea of sexual abuse. After the last session, I thought about my sexual feelings for my mother. I had this swirl of feelings of sex, death, and guilt. I realized I had a special relationship with my mother, which stimulated my wish to compete with and get rid of my father. In two dreams, I killed my father. Father was pushing me away from Mother into the real world. At the time I was wishing him out of the picture, he died.

"The only way I could get to the idea of sex in a 3-year-old was to think of sexual abuse. I was so happy to realize that I wasn't abused, that it was my inner sexual feelings. I was so relieved that I wasn't guilty of betrayal. I had knocked off a big dick. I had to assume its responsibilities. I gained the prize, but it was awful. I turned Father–Mother–God against me. I had to make amends. My self was too horrible to come out.

"Everything finally fell into place. I wasn't abused. I was the abuser. I thought Father's brother was going to nail me, and I was ecstatic that he didn't. The only source of solace was my mother's approval. The whole family was banished from paradise. In one dream, I killed my father with myself. I always felt I was hiding something and couldn't come clean.

"I searched for a perfect woman to give meaning to my life, to be like Mother, but her dark hair also meant a reconciliation with Father. Rejection by my mentor confirmed my betrayal of my father. Proof I couldn't get back into the kingdom. I felt excluded from the world of men, could only find solace with women. If I were myself, awful things would come out against my sexual self that have not been dealt with before. Here with you I got rid of the guilt with Father from a nonsexual part of myself. Incredible peace I felt the last three days. No regrets about the future. My courage is increased. I feel calmer, quiet, solid. I've gotten the lid off the last pot, in other words, my sexual self. I had a dream in which I shot my agent and was killed by a police officer, along with my mother. In a second dream I'm alive with a partner in a jail cell. We have a lawyer to defend us, but our stories differ."

Free Association: "My unconscious and conscious selves' idea of the truth. I feel like I got to the key, the bottom of the pit. I worked on it all weekend. It took a huge weight off my shoulders. I realized how important you are, my gateway back to the world of men."

At this point, the patient is sobbing in both relief and sorrow. He had now moved into further awareness of the oedipal conflict, but it would take him many, many months to work this through.

Next Session

In this session, the patient returned with a powerful confirming oedipal dream as follows: "A movie was being shot in Africa. There were alligators all around. There was a beautiful woman, very sexy, a girlfriend of the man shooting the movie. He was filming crocodile heads being chopped off in a meat packing plant.

"I was attracted to her. She asked me to dance, led me into the bathroom, took my clothes off, and made love to me. I was terribly turned on by her, but her boyfriend was outside the door. I said, 'Wait, we can work this out over time.' Her boyfriend entered with two other men. I was scared that I would have to fight them. He was huge. I hit him in the face and it had no effect. Before that, the woman had slipped, saying that she had wanted to dance with me, but actually said she wanted to marry me, and I was ecstatic. Then the man asked me if he was still the chief."

Free Association: "I needed reassurance that Father was still my father. I didn't have to move into that role. I often dream about being in the bathtub. Could I have had sexual arousal with my mother bathing me? I woke up this morning from this dream feeling fear, a deep sexual fear. It's that fear that made me think of sexual abuse. My relationships with women are like big-game hunting because I could get killed, too. My goal was to get my dick in and out without losing myself and my heart."

He then reported another dream. He loved another man. *Free Association*: "Fear of having my heart broken again as it was with my mother and father. I feared retribution and being heartbroken again. It all came apart when my father died."

In the next session, again his fear of retribution was presented in a dream. "I was a possessor of a powerful code that made me a target. The SWAT team was going after me. I realized I could be assassinated."

Free Association: "The code made me a target. In other words, getting myself back makes me a target. I woke up with fear again."

This led to further associations about his sexual feelings. "As an adolescent, I had a frightening recurrent dream. As I went to sleep, my thumbs swelled."

Free Association: "Terror relating to the penis, manhood. And another recurrent dream. Jesus returns and I am left with those who will be burned. I used to go asleep holding my thumbs in my fist. The women in my home were all very prudish. Desire and excitement led to fear. Women and acting scare me."

"Things I desire are unattainable for me. When I began to desire my mother, I wanted to get rid of my father. I lost everything. Mother, Father, sense of self. Ever after, afraid to want anything for fear of disaster and loss. Have to allow self to want what I want. That is the key. Must have been severely criticized by Mother early for what I wanted. Then later, I wanted Daddy out of the way. He died. I became a target of retribution. I didn't want to die. Now I have to do what I want, but I feel in the dark, blinded, and I lose it. The backwash is so powerful. It is so hard to stay with myself."

Next Session

Mr. L.'s awareness of infantile sexuality impels him to start reading Freud's *The Introductory Lectures of Psychoanalysis*. He then reported a dream that he was in a schoolyard and the students were masturbating in formation, like pilots fly. Then he was in a bar and the bartender was talking about how satisfying masturbation was.

Free Association: "I may have been criticized when playing with my penis in the bathtub. It was okay when Mother did it, but not me." He then reported another dream: "I was lying on top of my girlfriend talking to another woman on the phone about having sex. I penetrated my girlfriend, and she let me know she didn't like it because my penis was too small."

Free Association: "The next day, I had a vision of being pulled out of the bathtub and criticized for having an erection. Then I read Freud and the unconscious wish for Father's death became clear. No wonder I screwed up."

He reported another dream: "Another man and I were allowed to make love to this other man's wife. The other man pulled out without getting full pleasure, but I went into her and it was incredible sex. She said to the other man, 'You left without your charge.' "

Free Association: "This was a common saying by mothers about being billed. The man left without getting his money's worth. I'm afraid I paid too much for this oedipal satisfaction. I was afraid to enjoy sexual pleasure. Then, reading Freud, I saw these uncanny links between dreams and feelings and got in touch with how much I needed my mother's love. Sexual desire was an extension of that. Mother probably had good sex with Father, but in public she was critical of sex in general. I suddenly realized that my sexual awakening with Mother was normal, and it relieved my guilt."

"I began to have a profusion of memories, playing with my penis in the tub, criticism by Mother. As a kid, I didn't know how to masturbate, it was taboo. Severe criticism caused repression. I didn't know you could have an orgasm by hand until I was 19 when a girlfriend did it. My father was against thumb sucking and punished me for it. It became, 'Don't let an erection happen.'

"I was taking a shower and got in touch with how destroyed I was by these forces, but I laughed, how ridiculous. Desire and excitement associated with fear. Getting what I want associated with fear. At 19 I had my first sexual intercourse. An older woman, and I got an infection. This just increased the yoke of embarrassment. The first woman I had sex with was very dependable, like my mother. I couldn't get over the guilt about her—about deflowering her. Unconsciously, I sought retribution for this guilt. Then I said screw it, so what if I wanted to screw Mother. My alternative to masturbation was climbing a pole when I had an orgasm because of its rubbing against my penis without my having to touch it. I could do it in free space, but I can't do it with my hands."

Twentieth Month

In the next session, Mr. L. reported: "I felt good after the last session. Then I got a big IRS bill for $15,000 and the usual death spiral started—retribution for activating myself. However, this was different. I was able to use reality to limit it, a wonderful feeling of self-confidence that I could work it out rather than just lose."

He reported a transference dream after the last session: "You took over the 'Johnny Carson Show' and were very good. I passed you afterwards, said 'Hello' and you ignored me, but this was a sign of a special relationship."

Free Association: "I was trying to be entertaining for you but keeping my distance. What is transference? I keep a distance from you, have to do it myself to avoid disappointment, resented your charging me for a missed session. I have to look at it as an economic relationship."

I interpreted that he cannot relax and be himself with me for fear of disappointment and loss, so he becomes a very hard worker. He cannot allow himself to rely on me, so that I become an assistant to his hard work rather than a collaborator.

He replied: "I thought this week, 'What would happen if you died?' I've had several dreams of men dying, one dream of my uncle dying. I was a little boy and sad. When you're gone, I will have no one—I said to my uncle—for me to put my head in his lap."

I then interpreted that he reaches for Freud to have a father who is always there. Why does he need Freud when he has me?

He replied, "When it comes to relying on you, I pull back. I never had a collaboration. The idea of it is almost too irritating, something that I want but can't have. Collaboration is forbidden because of pain and loss. Maybe when my father died, I was glad. I would get the forbidden wish. I remember having no emotion when he died."

At the next session, he reported, "I felt lots of release of tension after the last interview. I felt light and clean. I'm understanding where the pain and guilt and shoulds come from. I feel I've turned a corner. I have dreams of feeling clean. I'm handling adversity with confidence rather than going into the usual death spiral."

A dream: "I shouldn't get married for four years."

Free Association: "I am getting me back. I want to try again. I want to find the perfect fantasy woman without fear of rejection and then counterbalance her with my girlfriend."

I brought him back to the prior session, pointing out that his need to deny the collaboration with me provided the same defensive function as the fantasy of the beautiful woman in the story, a fusion defense against full engagement of his self because of the fear of disappointment. Part of him seems to be saying, "I don't want to be myself because I'll have to give up this fantasy world, but the situation requires a broader context, that is, to step out of fantasy into reality."

He replied, "I'm still not into acting as I wanted to be, too scared to death of success. For me, desire and fear go together."

At the next session, he said, "I feel I can do what I want only after I do all the shoulds."

I interpreted this as a rationalization for avoiding self-activation.

He said, "I only realize this when there are so many shoulds around, I don't have time to do what I want. Work for me has this element of depression, but when I do activate myself it feels good, I get excited, and then I get depressed. It won't work, it will be no good."

I interpreted that self-activation leads to disappointment and failure. If he loves his mother, he will lose both his father and mother.

He reported a dream: "I was in an apartment with Mother's things around. I was so disturbed I woke up. Then I went back and had a second dream and she was there."

Free Association: "I had several dreams about Mother's coming back. There was a horribleness to it. She's supposed to be dead. I asked her what it's like. She replied, 'It's a lot of work.' "

Free Association: "Ugh! Even death is a lot of work. Work for me involves death and depression. My father, it was not that way with him. He loved what he did. If I get like him and enjoy what I do, I will die."

I interpreted that he avoids self-activation because he assumes he will die, but I confronted that this is a feeling, not a fact. And he treated it as if it were a fact.

He replied, "I had to sneak in self-activation in the corner so I wouldn't die. My sneaky feeling for Mother and betrayal of Father meant I couldn't come clean, nothing I could do."

I interpreted that the shoulds were to pay off this guilt so he can partially activate himself, that he is trying to find meaning in the corners in order to avoid the feeling of death.

He replied, "You're the only one who helped me understand that."

I confronted that he didn't lose that understanding but that he gave it up. Each time he activated himself, the anxiety about death emerged and he gave up self-activation and then moved to the shoulds; he's been aware of this in sessions for a long time, but similarly, he gives up the awareness as soon as he leaves the session and goes back to the shoulds, just as he did at home.

He began the next session: "If I keep doing my thing in fantasy, I can't be disappointed, and I can continue to avoid the anxiety associated with acting. I look at the acting, and what I feel is, 'I can't have that.' And, at the first obstacle, I give up because it reinforces my fear of disappointment. I back away immediately. My feeling is that I can't have or shouldn't have what I want and it repeats the loss of my father."

I interpreted that his avoidance of self-focus and self-activation maintains his anxiety about them—his fear that if he does so, he will die—from coming to the surface in sessions so they can't be worked on, like someone who's afraid of subways comes to treatment but never goes near subways.

He replied, "I'm only now beginning to believe that it can be okay."

Referring to his procrastination, I confronted that it seems to me that he is ready to move and that an artist is an artist by doing his art. I used the example of Joseph Campbell's talking about how the person who follows his bliss inevitably gets help from others, that he has been looking for "meaning" in books and dreams when really he knows what he wants to do and the only way to find meaning is to do it.

Regression and Interpretation of Transference

Twenty-first Month

Access to his oedipal conflict last month, this month impelled a real surge of self-activation externally, more interest in his acting, more interest in his girlfriend. This lasted a good part of the month, but then at the end of the month, he began to drag his feet. He talked about struggling to keep going. Just doesn't believe it could be any good. Got scared and pulled back. He began to have fantasies again about the ideal woman, which made him doubt his feelings for his girlfriend.

I interpreted. As he does well, he develops anxiety about losing the fantasy relationship he has in his head with his father. That this fantasy transference is being reenacted with me. That if he gets better, he will have to leave me, which will be like leaving his father and will lead to the same feelings of disaster. That he has to resolve these feelings about me as a substitute father in order to get better access to his own self-activation.

He responded, "I often have a dream of you as a replacement for a father, and that makes it safe to come out." He started to cry. I suspect that he cries because he is seeing the feelings of loss associated with separating from his fantasy of me as a father. A powerful part of his self-activation is his desire to leave his job at the bank, which he hates, and set up his own business.

Twenty-second Month

With his marriage to take place in several months, Mr. L. struggled with giving up his fantasy of the beautiful dark-haired woman, which at bottom was a fantasy of reunion with his father. "I have a desperate search for a woman to pull me out of the marriage. I feel dread every morning." And, also, he began to avoid self-activation more.

I interpreted, "It's more soothing to you to see it as giving up the relationship with the beautiful woman, rather than a difficulty with growing up and being on your own." He said that the only way to complete himself had been through this reunion fantasy with a beautiful dark-haired woman, who was a substitute for a reunion with his father.

Twenty-third Month

The fear of retribution persisted. Mr. L. reported fear of retribution from all authority figures. Interpretation of the fusion transference led to a return of the oedipal conflict. He reported dreams about sex with relatives—cousins, nieces; recurrent dreams of being in a bathtub, urinating in the tub, with a beautiful, dark-haired woman at the other end. "I kissed a woman who acted like she didn't need sex with me."

Another transference dream: "I ran into a nice old man who said I could do what I wanted, had faith in me, and I cried. I dreamed about my parents' bedroom, wanting to have sex with a woman there. I'm in the back bedroom, and Mother is bathing me in the tub. This turned me on, and then she hit me. I never masturbated until age 18."

Getting access to the oedipal sexual feelings stirs up feelings of retribution, guilt, and loss, the reunion fantasy of the beautiful, dark-haired woman began to recur, and the patient said, "As far as guilt is concerned, there is no redemption for me. I have the mark of Cain. Was I Judas and Cain, the betrayer and the murderer."

This led to more oedipal dreams. "I had a dream about looking forward to sex with a sexy woman, but she was married, and her husband was breaking down the door." *Free Association:* "In childhood, sex was associated with bathrooms and the back bedroom. In dreams, I tried to get women into the back bedroom for sex. Mother bathed and powdered me there. She may have prohibited my playing with my penis.

Father put metal jackets on my thumbs to stop my thumb sucking. Mother could be very punitive. I got either adoration or retribution."

This led to feelings of shame over masturbation and sex with women. "Thumb sucking was forbidden. I had recurrent dreams of my thumb getting big, and I awoke in fear.

"Recurrent dreams of the bathroom and the back room and sex. I masturbated a lot in college and I pursued sex with women, felt disloyal to my mother. I betrayed Father, and now was betraying Mother by having sex without marrying the women. So guilty and shameful, I couldn't live life."

This led to more oedipal wishes and castration fears. "I had a dream of trying to make love to a black maid. She was worn out and broken spiritually." *Free Association:* "Mother was the dark-haired woman. She was broken after Father's death." A second dream: "I playfully grabbed my brother's dick. He attacked my crotch, but I had a cup on." *Free Association :* "It's a fear of retribution from my father for feeling for Mother. Father's death fulfilled my desire to be alone with Mother. My desires are disaster and dangerous."

"I finally had a dream in which I had an erection and felt I was healthy for the first time." This led, however, to dreams of fear of competition: "I was beaten in a race. If I try to be myself, I'm beaten before I start." I interpreted the feeling that if he competes, he has to lose. *Free Association:* "There's a knife in me. If I move too much, it will hurt me. I just can't get in gear. I get more and more afraid as my marriage comes due."

Twenty-fourth Month

He married, and getting access to the oedipal material freed him to relate to his wife and the wedding in a realistic way. "There was no dark-haired woman at the wedding. I was very happy. It was the right thing to do. The barrier dropped so I could love her as I couldn't before. I had profound dreams of resolution with the father figure, and that I left the bank to set up my own business and it was okay. I felt calmer, more connected, and different about Father. I was a man, and he was a man. More confident, I can be a man, and disaster won't strike."

This self-activation continued to flower. "Marriage has anchored me.

My dreams of sex are more fulfilling, but filled with retribution. However, on my honeymoon, I had dreams of my mother's rejecting me, it seems, at my father's grave." *Free Association:* "I'm emerging from feelings about death and parents. I wrote a song of reconciliation with my father. What I pray for has happened, to be able to love and commit myself to a woman."

"I'm full of ideas for acting projects, and I have an intense urge to leave the bank, and then I panic. Acting is me, not a whim. I have to do it, and take the risk."

I did some communicative matching about risk by talking about Eisenhower's taking the risk to make the decision to land in Normandy on D-Day despite the bad weather.

Termination Phase Begins

Mr. L. began to talk for the first time about ending treatment. "I can begin to see the end of treatment. I'm scared to death, however, about continuing to move ahead."

I again did some communicative matching with Joseph Campbell's comment, "Follow your bliss and unseen hands will help you."

This led to dreams about lying in his father's arms, feelings of loss of his father. "I wrote a song, 'Love Denied,' about a love so strong, I couldn't shake it." This was folowed by dreams of reunion with his father.

Working through the feelings of loss of his father in the transference gave him access to the infantile love of a father, linking the current sense of self with its roots and integrating the infantile self with the adult self, resulting in self-activation in the song. Mr. L.: "Now I have energy that flows without cutting me up like a knife."

This forward movement led to dreams of infantile sexuality and sexual confusion followed by retribution. For example: "Attracted to an adronymous woman and found she had a penis." And "Dreams of lying on Father's chest, but was I a man or a woman?" *Free Association:* "The discovery of sexual differences and Mother's slapping my erect penis. I had to keep both sex and aggression down to avoid guilt. I had to change my identity. I was doomed. I had done irreparable damage."

This led to avoidance of self-activation, particularly in his acting, which I interpreted as a defense against the infantile sexual material in the prior session. He then explored the fear of wanting anything deeply because the desire would be dashed.

This then led to a castration dream. "There's a dirty wound in my foot. It's infected. It's rotting. It flashed through my mind that it was the end of my dick." *Free Association:* "I used to dream about something happening to my dick. A wound spitting pus to heal itself."

At this point, he has regressed to avoiding acting and becoming obsessed with the shoulds or his responsibilities. He reports, "The next morning, I woke up with the fear of being excited. Too much like a knife cuts my body." Then he persists with his acting and anger emerges.

He had a dream: "Some male friends are going to attack me for transgressing a code. Can't do what I want, and I woke up furious." A disguised transference dream about fear of retribution by me. It was not interpreted as it did not interfere with therapeutic momentum.

Twenty-fifth Month

In the next session, Mr. L. reported "a feeling of wholeness. Everything became clear. As a child, my first wishes were sexual. I played with my penis, and mother slapped my hand. Father attacked the thumb sucking. Then there was the desire for Mother, and competition with Father, but Father died. Made my wants terrible.

"The fourth powerful wish was to have father Back. I couldn't allow it up. Four desires: sexual, thumb sucking, Mother, and Father. I couldn't have erections, Mother or Father.

"In adolescence, dreamed of thumb sucking. I had to regain Father and lose him again here. We were father and son, kindred spirits, soul mates."

This led to exploration of how his wants were cut off, how he was kicked out of Eden, and left with a witch, his mother, with a great deal of sadness and feelings of loss. He explored deeper the feelings of loss of his father with a flood of memories and a feeling that all the pieces fitted together.

He had a dream about a huge shark on the beach, dying but still alive, and then realized there were 25 sharks lined up in front of his house. He was afraid to move. *Free Association:* "I used to fish with my father. He showed me the teeth of little fish. It's a fear of retribution and punishment. I've gotten in touch with the rough side of my father, which scared me. He made me do things that were unpleasant. He wasn't as easy to sway as Mother. It's a link to the fearful side of my relationship with him.

"I had these two sides, and I couldn't put them together. And when he was gone, I had my mother, and she was easier on me. A combination of my wishes for my mother reinforced by anxiety about Father's rough side."

I interpreted that he had idealized the positive relationship with his father to defend against his fears of retribution castration.

"Father challenged and introduced me to reality, and made me anxious, and reinforced the guilt about wanting Mother to myself. The shark is addicted, bites. Recall urinating with Father, seeing his huge penis. Revenge of the big dick. Roughness of Father, pulling me out of Mother's soft world.

"But Mother was also sharp, and could turn on me fast. I had buried the positive father with his death and recorded only the negative. Then I recorded the positive and idealized it as a protection against my negative feelings. Now my negative appears. We get a more balanced view."

After the shark dream, the patient had another dream of a prisoner having both arms shot off, which was related to the masturbation taboo and retribution.

Free Association: "Attacked by my mother for playing with my genitals, arms would be shot off. The attacking of thumb sucking by both parents. The dreams of thumb sucking in adolescence. It all ended in disaster. I felt guilt and shame for wanting to get rid of Father. At 6 and 7, I had dreams of being burned. The real self is buried deeper."

This led deeper into an exploration of his infantile grandiosity in the following dream. "The dark-haired woman was aging in the mirror, and then she turned to me." *Free Association:* "As a child, I looked at myself in the mirror. I liked what I looked like, and it soothed the inner me. But also, there was some self-adoration. I still look in mirrors and I'm surprised at how I look, as opposed to how I feel. I look to see who I am. Then I dreamed I was Robert Kennedy's Vice Presidential candidate. I had an inflated sense of self."

I interpreted that his father started to deflate his grandiosity with his mother, and when his father died, the guilt and the fear of the big dick prevented the patient from identifying with his father. He then lost his mother too, and regressed to recapture the grandiosity with his mother through the beautiful, dark-haired woman.

The patient responded, "I felt that self-adoration was another thing to be guilty about, even though I sought it for the moment."

"This led to a dream that I was unfaithful." *Free Association:* "All of my life I felt unfaithful. I would have relationships with one girl, and sleep with others. My wildest dream is to be myself and be successful. At 7 or 8, I became religious in order to deal with the guilt. I knew I was damaged."

He then reported some real-life events that had reinforced the feeling of God's punishing him. At his first sexual intercourse, he had contracted a venereal infection. In his first driving experience, he had an accident. During his first year in college, his mother was hospitalized.

Then he reported a second part of the dream: "I wanted to have sex with this other man's wife, but she was getting old." *Free Association:* "I always set up relations with women who adored me more than I did them."

He then had a dream about his father's roughness, and the fact that the idealized women to whom he had been attracted were shallow. *Free Association:* "I woke up enraged at my mind for making me afraid. It was demystifying both my mother and my father, and my fear was of being myself."

At this point in treatment, the patient, having married, is now self-activating by moving from working in a bank to working for himself. Associated with this, he has a dream of having to hide from terrorists. *Free Association:* "I have to kill my excitement to avoid the terrorists."

Twenty-sixth Month

The patient had a dream: "I was marrying my best friend's wife, and saw my own wife outside crying." *Free Association:* "It explores the close relationship with my mother and sister, my idealization of them, guilt about leaving them for my wife, and the second dream about kissing a woman turned into my mother, and Mother in flight with another man." *Free Association:* "Fear of retribution and rage. I had to cage my competitive anger. Too frightening. I killed Father. It was evil. I was evil."

I confronted: "You have to decouple the competitive anger from the fear of retribution and use it to support yourself."

Twenty-seventh Month

The patient at this point lost a large sum of money in an investment, which drastically reinforced his fears of retribution, and he spent a good deal of the month talking about it and avoiding his acting, being preoccupied with the shoulds and the dark-haired woman. In other words, he regressed to defense at this reality reinforcement of his fear of retribution.

Twenty-eighth Month

Mr. L. returned to work on his anger, which allowed him to explore more deeply his fears of abandonment. "I'm fed up with doing penance for my crime. My anger was evil, not to be tolerated. Then along came Father's death. Rage at the betrayal.

"I've overthrown a false god, there is a sense of the air clearing a weight off me. How to stand up for myself."

This led to a dramatic dream: "I'm in my mother's bedroom. I thought she was in bed, but she was gone. I didn't know where she was. I called out to her. A bubble of sorrow and terror broke, almost drowned me. I realized it was pure stark terror of being abandoned, and at the same time, sorrow that she was gone. I've been dreaming before that she was still alive, realizing she was dead. This was the first dream of her just being gone. Father was gone. Now Mother was gone. The way I felt at age 4. I woke up shaken."

A second dream followed: "I'm ready to have sex with a woman in the office. I put on a contraceptive. Then I am with an old woman friend who reminds me of my mother. She was trying to get me upset. I left as the relationship was too sick, really like leaving my mother. I felt okay, no guilt or retribution. Then I was fooling around in my father's attic, which was his temple, and I found the severed head of a dark-haired woman, like my older sister, a beautiful, dark-haired woman. The fantasy has ended."

After the abandonment dream, the patient had a transference dream: "I also dreamed of your talking with me in my music room. You began to talk. I was feeling overwhelmed and relieved that you talked, and that you might help. You said, 'You see how unhealthy it is to have a relationship with your mother like that.' We were laughing, and had distance from it. I'm looking back."

I interpreted that he had been holding on to his mother to defend against the anger and guilt about his father. Getting access to the anger and guilt, he could give up clinging to his mother and the dark-haired woman to deal with his fear of retribution.

He responded: "The sense is dawning that I've a right to be angry about it all, especially the cowering and fear about my anger. I finally got fed up with it. Angry about not having done what I wanted to do. Not having harnessed my talent. The machine is disconnected from the drive train. The fear of my anger came from fear of retribution from my father. Also, if angry at Mother, she would fall apart, plus I had to avoid sexual feelings, and that's why I didn't masturbate."

This was followed by a dream of being back at college with friends and having a good time. *Free Association:* "It's the last time I was in the right place, in gear and supporting myself." He continued: "I realized how many years those voices have been there. I finally had found some peace. The past can't hurt me now. It was a gorgeous night. Remembered the ache and yearning for union with the universe I used to feel. No longer felt that. Trying to get out of myself and merge with it. I've given up on struggling for salvation. I was free, whole, and peaceful. Never felt it before. I was real, like I'd come home. A warm sensation in my chest kept saying its me, 'I'm here,' like a good friend was with me."

This was followed by another dream of losing money in the market, a dream of retribution. His associations after the dream: "I fought back. I wasn't a loser. I wasn't a loser. I fought for myself. I said I was more valuable than any stock. Being and doing was much more important than having."

The work on the anger continued. He had a dream about being attracted to a woman, and then being attacked by a bully and having to fight him off. *Free Association:* "I'm tired of all this bullshit. Why do I keep fighting these bullies? Father wasn't there, and I had to take care of Mother's need. Anger is helping me fight the bullies. I feel I have to kill the bully."

The work on the anger freed the patient to self-activate better, to enjoy his acting, which led to the following dream: "I was on top of the Empire State Building. There were severe winds. The building was swaying. I was in an apartment with a beautiful, dark-haired woman. I tried to get out. The building toppled. The top of it crashed into our apartment. I grabbed her in sheer terror, and clung to her for dear life, the only thing I could do. I said, 'There's a part of me inside of you that I need.' " *Free Association:* "I realized how deep my commitment had been to my mother because of my guilt about Father's death. I would suffer along with her. By abandoning my suffering, I'd be abandoning her and her suffering. Mother's dreams were dashed. Couldn't do what she wanted. I'm sure it was my fault, and my dreams had to be dashed too." I asked, "What did you put inside your mother that you needed?"

He replied: "The sins of wanting, desiring, selfishness, and selfhood were all confused. There was a taboo of selfishness. I confused being myself with being selfish. I exorcised the guilt about selfishness by focusing on her and giving up the self. My siblings taunted me about being selfish. My father's death put a lid on my struggle for myself. It was evil to be self. It killed my father. It caused my mother to be abandoned. To deal with it as part of myself, I poured myself on my mother and focused on her. Then religion was added on top."

I interpreted that he was caught between being evil and losing himself. He responded, "Guilty of killing my father and abandoning my mother, plus memories of being with my father in his workshop." The patient was now crying, "My mother stifled my mourning, so I had to stifle it also."

This then led to the following dream: "I fell in love with a sexy woman, a friend of my wife's. We were both attracted to each other, but my wife came between us. A woman tried to talk both of us out of it. It was the soul-merging type of love. I tried to remember the sexual moment. It was too good to remember. Sexual merging, she was whole, complete, a vision of beauty. I could see a window into that world. To see it, and not be able to have it was heartbreaking. My wife returned, and the world went cold and gray from technicolor as the woman was gone.

"I was disappointed and depressed. Then I saw a real beautiful male bird and a beautiful female bird flirting with me. I said, 'There's no comparison between knowing that an object exists and experiencing it.' I woke up heartbroken."

I interpreted that this was a fantasy reunion with his mother to recover what he had lost; in other words, a merger to replace the hole in his chest and be complete again.

He responded: "Merger restores me. It restores my sense of self. I used to yearn for nature. Now I realize it was for a relationship with a woman to recover what I lost. I am who I am. I felt I was seeing the world the way my father had. That's what killed him."

He then continued to have dreams of sex with married women, which were followed by attacks by men.

I interpreted that supporting himself leads to a desire for his mother and to kill his father, and is synonomous with that and the treatment, which implies that self-activation is giving him the gun to do himself in. But what he does is to split the desire from his mother and the hostility toward father, and dreams about one or the other, whereas actually they go together.

He responds, "If I engage in the real world or self-activate, I will die."

Twenty-ninth Month

Mr. L. now shifted from sex and aggression to work through his wish for a preoedipal father to take care of him and an oedipal father to love and forgive him. He dreamed: "Abraham Lincoln stopped me from destruction. Then Robert E. Lee loved me and me him. I was so encouraged to be able to relate to these men, even in defeat." *Free Association:* "There might be other men in the world who are like them, and with whom I could be me. Were there other people in the world like me? They didn't all have to be sharks or CPAs. I woke up in fear that my apartment house was burning down, but I escaped."

I interpreted that the dream was a wish for reconciliation with the two men who knew tragedy and despair and helped to connect him with the world of men. At the same time, I interpreted that he continued to avoid his feelings about me.

He replied, "I'm scared to death about loving a man. At the thought of ignoring you, I cried about my father's not being there and got angry. Why do I have to do this?"

I interpreted that he denied his involvement with me in the therapeutic alliance, although he lets me into the transference to defend against the fear of investing himself in me and being disappointed again. His reply: "I also don't want to rely on anyone else in order to keep the shrine of my father alive. I feel relief that there is someone to help me, but afraid to rely on it. Evokes the childhood memory of relaxing on my father's shoulder, and hadn't been able to do it since." The patient is now crying.

I pointed out that allowing me into his emotional life will let him finish the mourning of his father here.

He returned to: "I'm feeling light, burdenless, clear."

Mr. L. reported: "I had a dream of myself as being whole, healthy. A window opened to the world I lost, but I had changed." Then he reported the following dream: "I hugged Al Pacino, said I loved him." *Free Association:* "I had felt shut out from manly love. I pumped myself up. Then I thought about a woman to whom I gave herpes." This is probably a metaphor for hurting his mother by killing his father. "These were the last darkest secrets I had. I'm afraid that if I become successful, I'll be hit with the guilt."

This is followed by a dream of acting in which he felt a glow, followed by "being in a dark room alone, a lead ball on my chest." I thought the first dream was a dream of self-activation, followed by a separation dream, with the depression that goes with it.

Thirtieth Month

Working through the relationship with his father leads to self-activation and involvement with acting, expressing, "It's the first time I ever felt confidence in myself." This led to dreams that brought out the history of his life before his father's death, and various losses that he had experienced in junior high school.

Thirty-first Month

In the 31st month, he has oedipal wishes alternating with a dream of his mother as a young woman, as a lover, as middle-aged, and then as dead. *Free Association:* "I knew she was leaving, and she said, 'Stay in my heart.' I finally feel a sense of entitlement and rightness to my own path without the feelings of doom and gloom, and I am starting to have thoughts about stopping treatment."

The self-activation continued through the 32nd month, when he had completely moved out of the bank and was operating his own business.

As might be expected, this led to an intense oedipal dream, as follows: "The woman I long for is pregnant. She was having it without me. I was afraid she'd demand money. I was a student. I was responsible for this, self-indulgent. It led to disaster. I wanted to search her out to figure out what to do. She was elusive, and I felt helpless.

"I felt fear and dread. Pregnancy always was a fear. I had to marry and it ruined my life. Yesterday, I said I was ready for children. This part of my psyche is telling me I'm not ready. I have to drag it with me. However, I'm less susceptible to other women. My love for my wife is secure. I'm ready to have a child.

"But in the dream, the beautiful, dark-haired woman is rebelling, haunting me, not going to let me get away with this. Yearning used to be such a problem for me, for my father, for women. The wish for reunion has decreased.

"So nice to be around an attractive woman without being driven to screw her, feeling it was sinful, trying to recover what I'd lost through sex. Dick was an ache that only stopped when it was in a woman. I'd been banished from paradise because of a sexual desire for Mother, which killed Father. Like Adam and Eve, recaptured that loss through sexual intercourse, overcame banishment, and had reunion with paradise.

"Thought I'd never get married because I had to search for the fancy beautiful woman. Never be monogamous. Called it chasing my tail."

Thirty-second Month

For the next several weeks, Mr. L. again became more self-activated and more involved with his acting. In the 33rd month, his self-activation led to a reenactment of the father side of the oediptal conflict with me in the triad in the following dream: "I felt vulnerable, fearful, alone in the devastated dark house." *Free Association:* "I felt no protection.

How I felt my whole life, unprotected, alone, abandoned, and a disaster. Then I had a second dream. I am with you, and you had a book. It was a casual setting. One of my legs touched yours. At the next interview, you left. A woman doctor was there, and tried to seduce me. I thought, 'Seducing your patient is the oldest ploy in the world.' She gave me the creeps. I went home, and a man tried to mug me. The cops chased him away."

I think these two dreams are the patient's self-activation interrupting his transference fantasy with me as a father, and, therefore, he feels vulnerable and alone, but I did not interpret it at this time.

Thirty-third Month

He and his wife are considering having a child. He is acting more, but it does continue to tap deep feelings of loss and fears of retribution and castration. He's dreaming more about acting and thinking of stopping treatment, but can't hang on to the inner conviction of confidence in the sense of self.

Thirty-fourth Month

The self-activation continued. Then he had a dream of trying to kill birds with rocks out of curiosity. *Free Association*: "The curiosity is what killed my father and hurt my mother. Therefore, my creativity was bad and wrong. When I practice acting, my ambition rises, and then I kill it."

This evoked memories of when his acting mentor dropped him, and how he was rewarded at the bank for his false self, and then he recognized that he had to get over the masterpiece syndrome in writing, in other words, everything he wrote had to be perfect. He then had a dream of flying a bicycle, He loved it, and brought it to a safe landing.

This was followed by a dream that, as a child, he was having acid poured over him. *Free Association:* "Exactly what I felt when my father died." Then he had a dream: "I was trying to rekindle an old flame. I was older. I lost my looks. I was an ogre. She was repulsed." *Free Association*: "The death of the young self, and the fantasy of the beautiful woman, 'Beauty and the Beast.' Female beauty would deal with the ogre and restore myself. I woke up with the deep sense of loss. I hated myself for killing my father. Then I had a dream about the nanny who really gave me my love of music."

Thirty-fifth Month

His becoming the father of his own child, in other words, replacing his own father, increased his fear of retribution, and he dreamed "a recap of loving, losing, and fear of retribution if I be myself." *Free Association:* "I had memories of losing my father's help at the age of 3 and being left in the clutches of a woman."

As a consequence of working this through in this session, Mr. L. started to feel better, decided to meditate, and to take life as it is. He decided that he can do both acting and the shoulds, but as the acting goes well, he becomes overstimulated and afraid he will crash.

He then noted that he's dragging his feet on following through. I thought that he was dragging his feet in order to preserve the fantasy fusion with me as his father, which I interpreted as his having difficulty giving up the idea of me as his father, and then I confronted that this was like the myth of Sisyphus: he rolls the stone up the hill, gets going, becomes afraid of losing the fantasy of me as his father, and then regresses. *Free Association:* His reply: "You understood me and it's the first time in my life and I don't want to give it up." At this point, I confronted that it's not enough to talk in the sessions, but that he must act, that is, he must do it.

Thirty-sixth Month

Mr. L. did better with his acting, and he said, "It's so great to be back in my own skin. No longer feel dead every morning. When things go wrong, I can stop the downward spiral. I feel so at home, fulfilled." Then he reported the following dream: "I netted a bird to let it go, and when I did, it died." *Free Association:* "I held myself down for so long, afraid that if I let go, I will die."

I interpreted that deeper involvement in his acting was letting his self go, which led to the fear that he would die.

Thirty-seventh Month

Improvement again flushed out the oedipal problem. He had a dream of sexual attraction to his mother, which was followed by a dream of a building falling on him, and of a craving for a dark-haired, beautiful woman, and of being an old man. There was also a loss of grandiosity. "As a child, I was treated as if I had talent, and I loved it." This was followed by a dream. "I had to attack and kill my mother before she killed me." Followed by a dream of sex with a married woman. Followed by a replay of his father's death and his mother's horror.

Thirty-eighth Month

The oedipal material continued with more access to his anger. He reported a number of sex dreams. *Free Association:* "Pussy no longer holds paradise."

He had a fight with a cab driver and showed enormous anger at being pushed around, which led to memories of being pushed around by his older brother and his mother. This then led to a dream about anger at a drunken man, which led to the recovery of memory since the time of his father's death. And then it began to open another door to memories before his father's death. And while all this was going on, he was not giving up in his life any more. Finally, he reported feeling that he betrayed his father by his wish for his mother and, therefore, he would never feel good again.

Thirty-ninth Month

Mr. L. reported that he was keeping disaster at bay by focusing on what he calls the shoulds; doing what he should do rather than what he wants to do, but he lost conviction about activating himself in a tidal wave of doubt.

I now confronted that he was treating his fears as a reality rather than a fantasy. He continued, saying that opening the door to memories before the death of his father led to his awareness that his mother had indulged his grandiosity, but his father hadn't, and it was hard to separate his real self from the feeling of grandiosity and being special. He ended the month with a dream of retribution.

I interpreted that he vacillated from a wish for the caretaker father to fear of retribution from the oedipal father.

Fortieth Month

For most of the month, the material led to depression and attacks on himself.

Forty-first Month

After working through the material on sex with his mother and on the death of his father, in this month, the patient began to show a clearing for the first time in three months and an emergence of his underlying aggression. He reported, "Outbursts of anger at men, my masculinity came back. I lost it to Father's death because I felt my aggression killed him. Became a 'nice guy.' Faced down my fear of aggression killing Father. Monster of aggression became my ally." In the course of this, there is also a parallel, recognition of the deflation of his infantile narcissistic grandiosity, and he has a dream of punching a police officer who had no credentials. *Free Association:* "I'm nearing the end of treatment."

I knew he was still avoiding self-activation.

Forty-second Month

Mr. L.'s improved affective state continued as his wife was about to have the baby, and a boy was born in the middle of the month. The patient reported: "My son helps to heal the loss of my father. I named him after my father. I'm feeling complete, like I haven't since my father died." Then he reported a dream: "A woman like my mother was threatening to leave me, and this was followed by a second dream of the death of the dark-haired woman." He then finally reported, "The only thing missing is the acting."

Forty-third Month

Vacation month.

Forty-fourth Month

The patient reported a dream: "I was on a sailing ship with a companion. We sailed into a cesspool. We would die in a pool of shit." *Free Association:* "When my mentor dropped me, I lost faith in my own fantasy."

He then tried much harder to follow through with his acting, which led to a dream: "The last woman with whom I was in love rejected me." *Free Association:* "I think this was a dream about my mother. I woke up with feelings of devastation and loss." This was followed by a second dream of a violent argument with his brother. *Free Association:* "Was it my father?"

Forty-fifth Month

"I wrote a song to my son about my father and cried for two days. The song brought out the hopelessness of trying to keep my father alive."

I interpreted that he was avoiding fulfilling himself in his acting to keep the fantasy of his father alive in the transference by acting it out with me. He replied, "It's about time I put myself on the line. I was a martyr, and I didn't realize it."

It appeared that he had worked through much of the problem of sex and aggression; however, now he was avoiding activating himself in order to keep the fantasy of the father alive by acting it out with me. He then began to work through the reunion fantasy with his father based on sacrificing himself. "It's cruel to have to let these memories go. I had made my mentor my father also."

Forty-sixth Month

Giving up the father fantasy led to feelings of loss of his father and mother, the wish to hold on to them. He's killing his father and losing his mother. His childhood was steeped in grief. Then he began to feel hope: "Now I see why I have been unable to commit myself to acting."

He seems now to be back to where he was 10 months ago after working through more sex and aggression. However, he still has not fully invested himself in his acting, and seems caught between grieving the loss and the fear of retribution.

Forty-seventh Month

"I had a dream of mummifying my father." *Free Association:* "I mummified my father to hang on to him." Then he had a dream that his father was spanking him. *Free Association:* "After Father's death, I felt like an evil cannon."

Forty-eighth Month

Mr. L. now acknowledged both positive and negative feelings about his father, which led to anxiety about competiion with his father, which then led him, as a defense, away from acting back to the shoulds, doing what he ought to do rather than what he wanted to do. He recalled his first sex, being haunted by fear of retribution. He had betrayed his father, and, therefore, couldn't want him back.

Forty-ninth Month

He's still trapped in the shoulds and recalled his positive feelings about his father, and then had dreams of being attacked and of mentors who failed him. I interpreted this as his reaction to my transference interpretation of using me as a father as a defense, which he experienced as another loss and disappointment.

Fiftieth Month

He continued to work through the loss of the fantasy of me as the father. "It's so hard to lose so many fantasies at one time." He reported regret at past mistakes.

I interpreted that he has been in an emotional prison, feeling guilty and punished. He can't have his dream, so he doesn't pursue it.

"I realize that nothing but acting will do it."

This led to more self-activation, more involvement with acting, and more mourning of his father's death. Dream: "The evil empire collapsed." *Free Association:* "Separated from my mentors, I have to do it myself, and I have fantasies of a father rescuing figure."

Fifty-first Month

The interpretation of the transference reunion fantasy followed by a real-life disappointment in his acting career led to profound feelings of depression and helplessness, of feeling abandoned.

I interpreted that he seems to expect his acting mentors to relieve his guilt about his father and approve of his self-activation, but in reality, the theater is a very tough world in which to be successful, and that what he has to do is become more persistent. This led to a remarkable change toward self-activation and involvement with his acting and further working through of the father reunion fantasy.

He tells me he is getting more into his acting. "Getting back in the game, but I wonder if I am too old. Then I realized that I didn't kill my father, but I still have to work through the loss. I still want him back, but I have to face that he's gone." Dream: "Fending off thieves to keep my father alive." *Free Association:* "I've had thoughts about stopping treatment."

I interpreted that if I am not going to be a father figure to him, he will have to leave me out of disappointment.

However, he got a decent acting job, followed by a dream: President Kennedy died and was reconciled with Governor Wallace. *Free Association:* "An acceptance of Father's death and reconciliation with him. I apologized to him. I seem to be becoming who I am through my acting.

Another dream: "The problem is fixed. I don't have to worry."

Another dream: "A crush on an attractive woman who says, 'I need an apendectomy,' but she goes off with a masculine man." *Free Association:* "Reconciliation with my father. Finally, at the end of the month, I am able to follow through. I feel at peace for the first time ever. I have reconciliation dreams. I wake up refreshed, rather then dragging myself out of bed."

Fifty-second Month

He reported, "I have a fear of getting what I want, and I had a dream of being a star." I interpreted that getting what he wants is taking the father's place with his mother, which leads to guilt and fears of retribution for killing his father.

He then reported a dream: "I'm on a high wire with a structure under it collapsing." I interpreted that if he is himself, he will collapse like he did when his father died. *Free Association:* "I was Adam expelled from paradise, and doing my acting feels like walking in quicksand."

This led to a dream of his mother's being alive, but not his father. "I haven't accepted her death. My life is good, but I still wake up in dread. I push down excitement feelings when I'm acting. Was I this excited at Father's death? It's a reconnection with my roots. How traumatic and lonely it was."

Fifty-third Month

The anxiety stirred up led again to regression to the shoulds, working around his apartment and avoiding acting. Then he had a dream of being eaten alive by a bear. He reported memories of closeness to his father and sadness at how impaired he had been, and then he had an intense oedipal dream, which I interpreted as that his wishes for sex with his mother and to get rid of his father made him feel guilty for betraying him and afraid of retribution. And to defend himself, he gives up, avoids self-involvement, and moves into the shoulds. An additional element is seen now in the shoulds. "I like doing work around the apartment." His father was a great do-it-yourselfer, and as a child, he used to accompany his father on these rounds so that the work projects are actually themselves both an identification with and a reunion with his father.

Fifty-fourth Month

Mr. L. is now again much more involved in his acting, but he said, "I have a profound distrust of living in reality." I interpreted that for him reality has meant retribution, that this was the 11th commandment for him.

Fifty-fifth Month

He returned to dreams about cheating himself. I interpreted that he was cheating himself in treatment by fusing with me as a father figure, and that he had to activate himself in his acting, as well as with me. "I still haven't forgiven myself for being glad my father died. I had to accept my betrayal."

Fifty-sixth Month

Vacation

Fifty-seventh Month

Having worked through, he again reported feeling wonderful about life, about his wife, his son, and acting. "Why did I feel so bad for so long? I'm having positive dreams." Then this quickly switched to another dream: "An overzealous prosecutor charged me with murder." *Free Association:* "By being happy that my father died, I betrayed him. My wants mean disappointment. Then I can step back and see how good life is." This was followed by a dream of being rejected by a dark-haired woman. "I couldn't contact her." *Free Association:* "I thought about finding out what university you taught at so I could contact you." *Final Dream*: "My father was dead and gone forever." *Free Association:* "Memories of my father's death and my mother's falling apart."

I interpreted this as a response to my interpretation about having to give up the fantasy of me as the father; that he feared my punishing him as he had feared his father's retribution.

Fifty-eighth Month

The patient reported having dreams of wanting to hold on to his relationship with me, his therapist and his father. Then he had a dream in which his father returned. "I had an adult relationship with him. I was calling out for Father in the night: 'Help me.' " Then a dream: "I was guilty about a murder I committed."

I interpreted that giving up the fantasy of me as father, stopping therapy, and activating himself were tantamount to having his mother and killing his father. Therefore, it evoked fears of retribution and the need to avoid acting to protect himself. There was also guilt about killing his father and leaving his mother by getting better. And this sends him back to the shoulds defense.

Fifty-ninth Month

Dream: "Death is coming for me." *Free Association:* "Finally I realized that this was a fear and not real. I can feel desire without feeling the loss of my father, acting, life, but I also continue to have feelings of guilt about leaving my mother."

Sixtieth Month

I continued to work on his giving up the fantasy of me as a transference father who would protect him, which meant ending treatment, which led to feelings of loss of the father, of fear, and of being emasculated.

Sixty-first Month

He began to come out of the fear, to activate himself more, and had a dream of being punished for sex. I interpreted at this point that it was not sex but activating himself in treatment with me, rather than reenacting his relationship with a father. Then he had a dream of a turning point, leading to an oedipal dream, nine dreams of sex and retribution, followed by dreams of more self-activation, then the wish for his father's or my benediction, dreams of overcoming the temptation of sex, of being whole, and then being exposed to retribution.

Sixty-second Month

Clearly overcoming the defensive reenactment of love and fear in the relationship with his father with me caused the underlying castration fear again to surface. He reported that the fear had increased, everything is the end of the world. "Had a dream that an older man had died."

Free Association: "I think it has to do with my giving up the notion of you as a father. Stopping treatment means the death of Father, which leads to fear and the avoidance of my acting." He also reported feeling rage at my interpretation, which he felt as a retribution. By the end of the month, he is back to his acting, and has a dream that "the structure is sound," and he has thoughts of joy for the first time.

Sixty-third Month

He reads and gives to me short stories "to exorcise the childhood trauma plus his memories at 6 and 15." Throughout the month, he reports continued improvement in self-activation, and his dreams are positive.

Sixty-fourth Month

The improvement of self-activation continues. He reports that now he feels that by activating himself and taking responsibility for involvement, he's purged of guilt and the fear of retribution.

Sixty-eighth Month

Mr. L. reports, "Ease is coming into my life. It's wonderful to be without depression. The pain and the power of compulsions have attenuated, my strength has increased, barriers are dissolving. Can't believe my good fortune. I feel love for my wife and son and my acting. My wife is pregnant again. I'm losing the feeling of fate as retribution. I do have choices and I can activate myself. My fun side is emerging, neither special nor vulnerable and being expressed in my acting." At this point, the patient seemed to be dragging his feet about cutting down on treatment. I brought it up, and he decided to cut down to once a week.

Sixty-ninth Month

"I'm on a roll. I'm focusing on my acting and getting more involved. That's what I've wanted to do all my life, ever since I was 10. I saw my uncle's picture smiling at me. I felt it was my father smiling at me. Retribution has turned into reconciliation and a peace fell over me, and I had some dreams."

Dream: "The house where I grew up was rotting and about to collapse."

Free Association: "My past—I'm not sad about its collapsing."

Dream: "Reunion with my father and myself as an adult."

Free Association: "Father wanted to be with me—I knew we would have to separate, but it was positive and joyful."

Dream: "A woman trying to seduce me—told her I was married."

Free Association: "I'm fighting my oedipal wishes."

Dream: "Wife and I are flying on a horse, exciting, dangerous—could have gotten off, but decided to stay on."

Free Association: "I'm acting for life and my wife."

Seventieth Month

"I find I can now hold, at the same time, feelings about my life before my father's death and after—able to separate the past and the present for the first time. A voice told me I didn't have to go through that loss again. I woke up happy to be alive. Had dreams of a dark-haired beauty beckoning to me—I told her, 'No! I love my wife.' "

The patient has now grown a mustache and a goatee.

Seventy-first Month

Mr. L. continued to report progress. "I'm on a roll. My work here is done. I'm becoming optimistic, I have a sense of well-being, happy to be alive, involved in all areas of my life, business and acting are going well, I love being able to soothe my son's anxiety by being there as my father couldn't with me. He lets me see my own situation better. I still have oedipal dreams, but they seem to be more contained."

He then reports having been angry with me for charging him for a missed session, but not bringing it up. Reported that he felt that his anger had killed his father, and his mother was always so harsh and attacking about anger that he was afraid of being eviscerated because his father's death and his mother's anger cut so deeply. His wife is pregnant with their second child, due in a month or so.

Seventy-second Month

Mr. L. reported getting angry at himself for not winning a tennis match, which led to rage at his father for not being there. "I was always so fearful of his retaliation." *He then reported a dream*: "You introduced me to a male actor; we got on well together and then we went our separate ways." *Free Association*: "You introduced me to my real self and to acting."

"Later, when I was angry, I dreamed that you were speaking to the public on the street corner—it was another you than the one with me. I asked a question and you said, 'I don't know who you are but you do know the answer.' I was angry at you for not knowing my name, but reassured that I knew the answer." *Free Association*:: "I'm coming to terms with your clinical objectivity, you're not going to be my father, your letter moved me" (He missed a session and I wrote him a letter.)

"Feelings of foreboding about leaving you. However, my business is doing well. I saw a photo of my parents and said, 'I'm okay now.' My job is to be a good husband, a good father, businessman, actor. Six years here—what a struggle. Now it's okay. First couple of years, I thought that you did nothing."

End of Treatment

DISCUSSION

This case clearly demonstrates two issues: the direct sequence I have called the essential dynamic of the personality disorders (i.e., self-activation leads to anxiety and depression, which lead to defense) and the clarity of the oedipal conflict once its defenses have been overcome.

The patient's presenting picture was of a closet narcissistic personality disorder with clinical difficulties, with avoidance at work and the pursuit of an idealized fantasy in relationships with women. The defensive segment of the patient's self triad was reinforced by the loss of his father and the subsequent abandonment by his mother, both occurring at a point at which, developmentally, the patient had just begun to enter the oedipal phase. The oedipal guilt about the death of his father reinforced the preoedipal guilt about focusing on the self rather than idealizing his mother.

Soon after the psychotherapy started, interpretations of narcissistic vulnerability opened up the heretofore hidden dissociative defenses against his father's death and his mother's subsequent abandonment. Again, some might see it as denial, but to me the total exclusion from consciousness argued for dissociation; that is, the memories were dissociated from the mainstream of consciousness.

The loss occurred at 40 months of age as the patient was shifting emotional investment from his mother to his father, barely entering the oedipal phase. The loss was so painful that he had to dissociate his feelings about the positive nature of his relationship with his father. The loss was further compounded by the loss of his mother, who fell apart at the same time, and the fact that he had to focus on her to help stabilize her. Beyond that, his mother's problems recurred at every subsequent developmental stage.

After the dissociative defenses were worked through, the narcissistic defenses came to the fore: avoidance at work, pursuing defensive idealized fantasies with women, and "the shoulds." The patient's working through of the dissociative defenses against the loss of his father and mother led to the recapturing of his earlier lost, grandiose self, which was, however, a false sense of self. He would have to work through the abandonment depression associated with the grandiose self and the earlier developmental arrests associated with his mother. This would enable his real self to emerge and replace the false self and lead to the oedipal conflict, reinforced by the death of his father. The sequence of the work seemed to support this view. In other words, he initially overcame the dissociative defenses, the sessions consisting of mourning where he discovered for the first time how powerful his positive relationship with his father had been and his guilt about the death. As the mourning subsided, its place was taken on center stage by his narcissistic defenses against the abandonment depression, and this led to working through his feelings about the loss of his mother and the recapturing of the grandiose self. This recurrently recalled the earlier real losses so that the real-life death continued to haunt the working through of the abandonment depression.

After much working through of the abandonment depression, the painful affects persisted, so it was necessary to explore deeper into the earliest narcissistic relationship with his mother before the loss of his father.

This led to the awareness of infantile feelings of sex, fear, and guilt. A mutual initial assumption at that point was that this was probably the result of some early sexual abuse. However, this did not hold up under investigation, as the investigation led instead to oedipal wishes and fears of retribution, that is, castration and death. These then reinforced the abandonment depression and the triad of the disorders of the self.

As the real self emerged, and the patient moved into the oedipal stage, the abandonment death theme was replaced by the death theme of the oedipal castration complex; the oedipal wishes for the mother, and the anger at and fear of retaliation by his father.

He defended against the anger and the fear of retribution in the transference by projecting a reunion fantasy on me as a positive father figure. This projection had to be consistently interpreted as a defense to bring him back to working through the oedipal wishes and the fear of retribution.

The question can be raised here as to why he did not work through the anger and the fear of retribution in the transference. An argument can be made for the fact that in the normal oedipal phase, the child has the love of a father as a framework against which to work through the fear of retribution. This patient's father died at this crucial stage of his development so there was no father there to provide a support for working through the fear of retribution. Beyond that, he felt that it was his anger and wish to replace his father that had killed his father and devastated his sense of self. In addition, his mother had consistently attacked him for feeling anger. It may be that, to some degree, he required this fantasy figure in order to work through the oedipal fears and wishes in his dreams, memories, and affects.

The clinical proof of this is the overcoming of the oedipal fears and wishes, the final disappearance of his fearful projections and oedipal wishes, and the emergence of his ability to love and work with minimal impairment by oedipal conflict.

Countertransference feelings are seen in my premature interpretations early in the work and perhaps a positive countertransference that inhibited my being aggressive in interpreting enough of his defensive positive father projection, although I certainly was aware of it and did concentrate on doing it.

I was unaware at the beginning of treatment of both the dissociative defenses and the oedipal conflict until they emerged. However, by keeping my focus on defenses and not trying to anticipate or lead the patient's content, I allowed it to emerge through the patient's efforts uncontaminated by any suggestions by me. It demonstrates, it seems to me, the effectiveness of this approach that stresses a focus on defense to protect the patient's content from being defensively distorted by the therapist. This creates the conditions that allow patients to bring forth the content on their own, thereby potentiating their then accepting its validity and working it through.

Follow-up Interview: 19 Months After Treatment

Mr. L., now 43 years old, was well groomed, relaxed, neither anxious nor depressed, and spoke freely about the last 19 months.

Work

The patient has continued to run his own business, which is moderately successful. Several temporary reverses led to episodes of depression, but, "I didn't feel singled out by the universe for personal punishment, and unlike before, I sprang back quickly."

"There remains, however, some lack of faith in the future that impels me to impulsive business decisions, but it happens much less now than before."

Theater

Some inhibition of individuation remains, as I haven't been pursuing my acting career as aggressively as I might. I seem to use business and the children as excuses. However, I am much more active in the production and direction side of the theater, putting together deals."

Affect

The patient denies any significant anxiety or depression (except as noted above). There are no sexual dreams, or dreams of being attacked. He has no fantasies or dreams about the beautiful, dark-haired woman. There are much less anger and much more freedom to confront others when necessary.

"The 'shoulds' are still there but have lost a lot of their power."

Family

His relationship with his wife is comfortable and satisfying, and their sexual relationship is good. There are no outstanding conflicts, except that they both are working so much, and with the children added, they don't have enough free time together. Their son is 4 years old, and now there is a daughter who is 1½. No outstanding problems with the children.

"I think I'm a good father. Infinitely better because of treatment. I felt profound and abiding satisfaction to be able to be with my son as he went through the age I was when my father died—3½. Our lives revolve around our children, which has its problems, but also is deeply satisfying."

Comment

The treatment brought about significant and enduring changes in affect and in object relations, while there remain residues of the problem with full individuation of the self. The grief over his father's death, the abandonment depression, and the castration anxiety, which were the focus of the treatment, are, for the most part, gone.

The patient has been able to commit himself to his wife in a loving and successful marriage and to be an involved and successful father. These are no mean achievements for a man who was previously unable to commit himself to a woman.

Problems linger in the full individuation of the self. At work, although moderately successful, he tends to get into trouble because of "impulsive decisions" based on a lack of faith in the future.

More important, he continues to have trouble with fully engaging himself in the theater. He doesn't avoid it; he is always involved at some level, but he doesn't throw himself into it either. This suggests some continuing need for defense against self-activation.

Of course, it would have been better if he were fully engaged in the theater. However, the clinical picture is never as clear as our theories. Perhaps it is expecting too much of a patient who suffered the loss of his father and the psychological abandonment of his mother at such a young age. Only time will tell. In any event, the treatment freed his self sufficiently for him to reenter the mainstream of life.

Chapter Nine

Intimacy in the Personality Disorders

Psychopathology and Treatment

Introduction

Therapists' concern with intimacy probably began with Freud's idea that the goal of treatment was to enable the patient to love and to work. The dramatic social changes we have undergone since the 1960s have heightened the issue of intimacy for the population in general, and particularly for patients with a disorder of the self.

The revolution of the 1960s against authoritarianism, racism, and sexism moved our society toward more individualism, female liberation, and the importance of an independent autonomous self. The female liberation movement reevaluated and redefined the mutual role expec-

*Adapted with permission from the *Evolution of Psychotherapy: The Third Conference*, edited by Jeffrey K. Zeig, copyright © 1997 by the Milton H. Erickson Foundation, published by Brunner/Mazel, Inc.

tations of men and women in intimate relationships toward greater equality and sharing.

The post–World War II generation who led this revolution applied it to child rearing. Their children, now adults, are carrying these standards out in their own lives. The profound effects of these changes on our views of intimacy are seen in the statistics: both parents working, later marriages, 50 percent of marriages ending in divorce. They are also reflected in the popular literature, in such titles as *Women Who Love Too Much, How to Get the Right Man, Intimate Partners, Cold Feet,* and *Peter Pan.*

Notions are bruited about that the new social model will be serial marriages—the first to have a child, and the second for an enduring relationship, or no marriage at all. This is despite the work of Wallerstein[9.3] and others on the profound emotional effect of divorce on children's development.

The ambiguity of these ideas is illustrated further by the prenuptial contract, which seems to be a contradiction in terms—two people who are getting together because they love and trust each other require a document based on mistrust. These social whirlpools complicate the issue of intimacy for everyone but they most strongly reinforce the problem for people with disorders of the self, because difficulties with intimacy have always been a key feature of the disorder.

Definitions—The Self and Intimacy

Webster defines intimacy as "a state marked by very close association, contact familiarity engaging one's deepest nature."

The developmental self and object relations definition is the capacity to commit the real self to an object through feelings of love and sexual attraction; to see that objects as a whole, both good and bad; to support the object's real self in a close, ongoing, enduring relationship with minimal impairment from fears of engulfment or abandonment; and to sustain that commitment despite feelings of disappointment or frustration.

The capacities of the real self, which emerge as the self becomes autonomous, make a vital contribution to the capacity for intimacy. They include such capacities as self-activation, soothing, spontaneity, sense of self-entitlement, acknowledgement of self-activation, continuity of self, capacity to see the object as whole, capacity to be alone, to tolerate anxiety and depression, and to commit to the object and to mourn loss of the object. One has to have an autonomous, whole self to more or less freely commit to the object.

The Development and Function of the Self's Capacity for Intimacy

The self's capacity for intimacy emerges and evolves through the stages of separation–individuation or through the stages of subjective self and verbal self to the oedipal stage, and is then tested and refined during adolescence and adulthood.

In the separation–individuation stage, the self emerges and develops to take on its full capacities. A successful separation–individuation stage leads to the emergence of a whole self representation with a relationship of mutual trust between the self and the object—the self having a realistic sense of entitlement of support and realistic sense of life's difficulties and frustrations.

There are differing views of how the emergence of the self occurs. Mahler[9.1] considered the chief issue to be separation of the image of the self from that of the mother, and described the child as going through four stages. Stern,[9.2] on the other hand, who thinks that the child is able to perceive the mother as separate from birth, sees the key issue as the self's capacity to become autonomous, whole, and to take on its functions. Stern described the self as going through four stages: core self, emerging self, intersubjective self, and verbal self. Both of these researchers, however, agree on one fundamental consideration: In order for the self to emerge and become whole there has to be, as Mahler reported, "a mother providing supplies and support for individuation and for self-activation," and as Stern put it, "mother providing empathic attunement to the child's emerging self." Since there are no perfect mothers and no perfect children, there may be scars emerging from these stages that do not necessarily represent a diagnostic disorder but rather minor difficulties with capacities for autonomy, creativity, and intimacy. And what person does not have a problem with one or another of those capacities?

Completion of the separation–individuation stage, which happens at roughly between 0 and 3 years of age, leads to the oedipal stage. The child enters this stage with an autonomous self and the capacity to see the object as a whole. The child then invests the parent of the opposite sex with sexual and affectionate feelings, which take precedence over the formerly one-dimensional view of the parent as caretaker—in other words, the relationship becomes sexualized and competition arises with the same-sex parent.

These conflicts submerge under the force of repression during the latency period, roughly from 5 to 12 years of age.

With the onset of the sexual drive in adolescence, these conflicts re-emerge. Then, guided by the incest taboo, the residues of unconscious oedipal conflicts are worked through by turning from the parental objects to peer objects during sexual emancipation. Adolescent experimentation in the external environment then takes place to achieve two goals: to establish an inner sexual identity for the self and to identify the intrapsychic sexual object that fits that identity.

In early adulthood, with sexual identity identified and the intrapsychic sexual object defined, the last task is to experiment in the environment in order to find a fit between the external object and the internal object—as Freud emphasized, the finding of the object is really a re-finding. The individual tests the waters with the object and evaluates the object's response. As the object's response is positive—supportive of the individual's self—interaction of mutually supportive real selves occurs, leading to physical intimacy. Physical intimacy leads to fulfillment of the search and completion of the cycle. The romantic and sexual idealization that accompanies "falling in love," although strongly based on fantasy, facilitates the process and eventually gives way to a more realistic and enduring relationship based on the gratifying interaction of the two selves. Of course, this includes both the sexual and the romantic interaction.

This pathway to intimacy is gradual, based on the mutual need to test the other and to protect one's own healthy narcissistic vulnerability. Sex is such a powerful drive to emotional intimacy that it can cement a close relationship, and used prematurely it can often make closeness impossible by aborting the essential testing aspect of the relationship necessary to establish a real relationship based on knowledge and interaction.

The Illusion of Intimacy in Disorders of the Self

For a patient with a disorder of the self, intimacy is a demand for real self-activation, which evokes separation anxiety, which evokes defense. These patients' impaired real selves, lacking autonomy and also lacking trust in the object, cannot tolerate or manage a real intimate relationship because it evokes their fears of being engulfed and/or abandoned. In order to be able to experience feelings of closeness and sexual gratification, they have to devise a defensive system, which, on the one hand, protects them from the fears and, on the other hand, allows feelings of closeness. They always titrate the one against the other—not so close as to stir up fear, and not so far as to lose the feeling of closeness.

This appears in the clinical evidence as follows: the borderline by clinging and/or distancing defenses against these fears, the narcissistic disorders by the need for mirroring defense of the exhibitionistic or the idealizing defense of the closet narcissistic disorder, the schizoid disorder by the need for a master–slave or self-in-exile defense. Each produces its own distorted illusion of intimacy: The borderline patient defines intimacy as a relationship with a partner who will take over responsibility and offer approval for regressive behavior. The narcissistic patient defines intimacy as being admired or adored or "basking in the glow" of the idealized other. The schizoid defines it as being in perfect compliance with the object in prison, but connected. The illusion is created by these patients that the relationship "works."

What they mean is not that there is a more or less harmonious mutual sharing of real selves but that their defense has been put in place, which allays their fears and thereby enables them to feel affection and sexual excitement as long as they continue to deny the maladaptive defensive aspect of the relationship. This can be seen clinically by the following types of relationships.

The Illusions of Intimacy

Partial Relationship

The patient establishes a relationship with a significant other who is not in reality available for a number of reasons. The other may be married, or a workaholic, or a traveler, and so on. The advantage of this relationship is that because the other is not available in reality, it does not evoke the patient's fears of engulfment or abandonment and then it is possible to experience feelings of love, sex, and romance without being impeded by these fears. For example, two couples are on a cruise together, and the man in one couple starts an affair with the woman in the other couple. At the end of the cruise, the man of the one couple has fallen in love with the woman and tells her he is about to divorce his wife. The woman in the other couple says that's fine for you, but if you ever get married again, look me up.

Instant Intimacy

The testing and trial period essential to the establishment of a real relationship evokes such enormous separation anxiety with these patients that in order to relieve that anxiety, they abort the testing process and jump prematurely into a relationship. It's a common experience to start treatment with a borderline patient who is not in a relationship and shortly thereafter the new patient meets somebody at a bar, has a sexual encounter, and they're living together. The function of this particular kind of intimacy is a defense against the anxiety evoked by the therapeutic relationship. The patient then titrates the one relationship against the other. As increasing therapeutic involvement evokes separation anxiety the patient moves closer to the other relationship. Fortunately, the instant intimacy has made the patient deny the destructiveness of the partner, which eventually emerges and can be dealt with by the therapist.

The Clinging Relationship

Marriage or the relationship established to avoid individuation: This commonly occurs when individuals pass through nodal stages in the life cycle that require more individuation—for example, leaving high school, graduating from college. It is at this point, when they will have to function on their own, that they reach out for a partner to defend against the anxiety that having to function on their own evokes.

Distancing Relationships

This occurs in a variety of ways, from no relationship at all to relationships that are distant. For example, one partner is away a good deal of the time. A good clinical example is of a couple, one of whom lived in New York and the other in London, who began dating across the Atlantic Ocean and then made the mistake of deciding to get married. The man left London, came to New York to live, and once the distancing defense was overcome, in a very short time, the couple were at each other's throats.

Sex Without Emotional Involvement

One example is sexual promiscuity with the rapid progression of sexual partners without any emotional investment, or sex without emotion with the same partner.

Emotional Involvement Without Sex

Relationships formed on the basis of mutual clinging that do not involve sex.

Narcissistic Patients

The patient who is unable to find the perfect mate, or the couple who get together on the basis of mutual idealizing that leads to mutual disappointment.

Sadomasochistic Relationships

Where the partner is used for the reinforcement and discharge of sexual anxiety and tension.

The Couples Who Fight but Stay Together

The question often arises—when a couple fights so much why do they stay together? The answer, of course, is that they stay together because they fight so much. The message is that it is preferable to have an external negative object on which to project the internal negative object rather than to have to contain and feel the depression and negative feelings associated with one's own internal object. The relationship suffers but the patient maintains more intrapsychic comfort.

There seems to be a relationship between the degree of negativity of the internal object and the need for an external object on which to project it. The more negative the internal object, the greater is the need to pick an external negative object.

What is illustrated here is how the need to reenact distorted internalized object relationships takes precedence and erodes the capacity to have a mutually satisfying intimate relationship.

The normal pathway to a relationship of experimenting and testing and evaluation of feedback does not occur. In the rosy glow of the idealization of sex and romance that occur in the early stage of any relationship, the patient throws caution to the winds in order to act out and often to reenact the internalized object relations. It is only later when the realities that were denied begin to impinge that difficulty arises. Incidentally, can you imagine what this normal idealizing process that occurs early in the relationship does to the already present clinging and idealizing defenses in patients with disorders of the self?

In working with these difficulties with intimacy, I found certain comments helpful. For example, I will say to a patient who distances: "You could walk through a room with 20 people, 19 of whom were available, and pass them all up and pick the one unavailable person." Second, to those who are using extreme denial of their significant other's negative aspects, I will often cite the movie "Some Like It Hot" where Joe E. Brown is taking Jack Lemmon, who is dressed as a woman, in a motorboat to meet his mother. Jack Lemmon does everything he can to discourage Joe E. Brown from this endeavor, and finally, when Brown is not hearing and not responding to these efforts, Lemmon flips off his wig and says, "Besides, I am a man." Joe E. Brown looks over calmly and says, "Well, you can't have everything."

One reliable method to determine whether a new relationship for a patient in treatment is adaptive and progressive or regressive and defensive is as follows: If the patient reports that the new person makes him or her feel so comfortable and so at ease, the answer is the negative. This is an object that provides defense. However, if the patient talks about being so attracted to the other, but also so nervous he or she can hardly sit still, this is a positive sign. This person is presenting the challenge of a real relationship, which evokes the patient's separation anxiety.

The Problem of Loss with Disorders of the Self

A whole self representation is necessary in order to be able to separate from a relationship and repair the loss through grieving. This takes time and frees the self to form a new relationship and can often produce emotional growth. For people with a disorder of the self, the end of a relationship is a crisis that reinforces their innermost fears of abandonment, and unable to grieve because of the lack of a whole self representation, they are forced to resort to their characteristic defenses—denial, detachment, acting out. These, however, do not free the sense of self, so they are left to continue reenacting the same scenario in future relationships. It is often astonishing to note how hard they strive to pick a partner who is different from the last, and who indeed on the surface seems to be different, but who inevitably turns out to be the same.

The Therapeutic Task

The therapist's task is to decode these defensive illusions and bring to the patient's attention that what he or she had felt was an expression of an intimate relationship was in reality an illusion consisting of defenses against abandonment or engulfment coupled with denial of the maladaptive part of the relationship.

Borderline Disorders of the Self—Problems with Intimacy

In the case of the borderline patient, relationships are dominated by the need to defend against the fear of abandonment depression; they will be unreliable, vulnerable to frustrations, and heavily dependent on the mood or feeling at the moment. The borderline lover will have trouble sustaining relationships because the loved one will be seen as two entities, one rewarding and satisfying, and the other withholding and frustrating.

There may be no continuity in the way the borderline views his or her partner. It shifts from moment to moment and is either totally good or totally bad. In any event, the loved one is never perceived as a complex, richly ambiguous person embodying faults and virtues simultaneously.

A Woman Acting Out Through Clinging

This was a 33-year-old attractive single woman who lived alone in an apartment close to her parents, did not work, and led a jet-set life with neither goals nor direction.

Chief Complaint: Depressed, with no self-esteem and destructive relationships with men. She could not seem to find an appropriate man and the men she did find eventually rejected her and she felt devastated. At age 27 she married a man who later became addicted to drugs and was arrested. Six months prior to coming for treatment she had been pregnant and engaged, but the man broke the engagement, and she was again crushed, had an abortion, and became depressed and suicidal.

Family History: Her father virtually ignored the patient as a child, but when she became an adolescent, he idealized her verbally without giving any support to her real self. Her mother demanded overtly and covertly that the patient give up her real self and take care of her. Any expression of the real self was devalued, attacked, and extinguished. The patient managed to get through high school, went away to college, got depressed, and began drinking and sexually acting out. She came home after one year and took a job in sales where she was fairly effective for several years.

Psychodynamics: The mother's lack of acknowledgment and attacks on the patient's real self led to an abandonment depression characterized by feelings of being smothered. She was engulfed as well by fears of being abandoned, and by a profound feeling of hopelessness about her wishes for support of the real self. The feeling of hopelessness about support was reflected back on her impaired real self; in other words, she was unloveable, and it was hopeless to try. Her only viable existence was through clinging to her mother and to unavailable men. The awareness of the hopelessness was defended against by acting out, and so she would pick inappropriate men and act out intense romantic fantasies through immediate clinging, denying the man's inappropriateness or unavailability.

She created an illusion of a real relationship, and because it was an illusion it enabled her to experience feelings of romance, love, and sexual pleasure, and to renew a sense of hope of being loved. Unfortunately, the inevitable, inexorable end of these misadventures—the man rejecting her—actually replayed in reality and thereby reinforced her deepest, most buried and defended-against fear—that she truly was unloveable and so there was no point in trying to be loved.

The central dynamic was to externalize, reenact, and replay the devastating loss she experienced in her early relationship with her mother in order not to feel and remember it.

As she controls her acting out, she says: "I have been trying to make a silk purse out of a sow's ear, don't I deserve more in a man? I used to feel that if I stood up for myself a man would disappear. I'm now defining the kind of man I want for the first time."

To illustrate the success of the internal realignment, she reported another blind date—"He was an attractive man, wealthy, but there's no chemistry between us—I'm not attracted to him—he's not up to my speed—not where I want to go in life—does not seem to have any life of his own and just because he is nice and attractive and has money is not enough." This control of the acting out leads to the depression and her negative self-image: "I feel like I'm a paraplegic from a car accident, lonely, depressed, hopeless. I hear Mother's voice saying I can't make it on my own, I'll fail and be rejected."

A Man Acting Out Through Clinging

This was a 50-year-old businessman married to his third wife.

Chief Complaint: "Although I'm successful at work, my depression has been getting worse for the last three years with suicidal thoughts—great conflict with my wife, whom I find demanding but boring, and I've lost sexual desire for her." Within the context of this depression there had been an upsurge of lifelong character problems: difficulties with self-activation, passivity, and self-destructive behavior in general—either clinging or withdrawing and provoking the object.

Past History: Mother was borderline, very depressed, clung to the patient, and after his birth, had several miscarriages. The father, judging by his behavior, seemed to have been either a narcissistic disorder or a psychopath. He was an alcoholic, had recurrent failures in business, ignored the mother and the patient, and exhibited blatant sexual acting out.

The mother viewed the father's narcissism and sexual acting out as expressions of masculinity, and while she tolerated it in the father, she vigorously attacked the patient's efforts at self-activation, masculine and otherwise, which reinforced his clinging. The mutual clinging reinforced oedipal conflict. Although he was chronically depressed, he got through the developmental years without clinical episodes but functioning far below his capacity. He barely made it through the last year of college and graduate school due to an avoidance of self-activation and work to defend against depression. Since that time, his work has been moderately successful. The first of his two wives left him, and he had two prior tries at psychotherapy without much improvement.

He described the intimacy problem as follows: His wife of five years was 40, a dietician. He described her as self-centered, demanding, attacking his self-expression, sexually unresponsive and refusing to have treatment. He tended to cling to her, acting out his wish for reunion, and the more he clung, the angrier his wife got, and the angrier she got, the more she withdrew, and the more he clung. His not setting limits encouraged her acting out of rage and shaped her behavior to be more and more like his intrapsychic object—making her a more suitable object for his projection and reenacting rather than relating.

Psychotherapy: The confrontation of his avoidance promoted self-activation. He attempted to do better at work and in social relationships but continued to avoid dealing with his relationship with his wife.

His depression increased as he activated himself but did not continue to deepen and memories did not emerge—he was individuating without separating. Confrontation then turned more rigorously toward his clinging to his wife and his denial of her attacks on him.

He began to curb his clinging to her and to take responsibility for himself as a husband in the marriage, setting limits to her narcissistic demands. This led for a while to an increase in her attacks, more conflict, and even less sex.

It also led, on his part, to guilt about assertiveness because he saw it as narcissistic or psychopathic. He could not decide whether his disappointment in his wife was due to his perceiving that she was narcissistic or to his perceiving that she was not narcissistic enough to serve his need to project an Amazon on her. At the same time, he dreamed of the need for an Amazon and a monster attacking him. He questioned, "What will I do without the Amazon? I need her to control and intimidate me."

He finally behaved more appropriately as a husband, stuck to his guns, and eventually stopped his projections. His wife, freed from this stimulus to resonate with his negative projection, settled down. The attacks stopped, and the relationship improved. Next, combined preoedipal and oedipal sexual conflict came to center stage.

The patient complained of the lack of sexual response, trying to force his wife into treatment. She refused. I asked him why he didn't discuss problems with her in detail and tell her what he wanted. I mentioned that every time he asserted himself, she had more or less responded. She did respond to his discussion, and then his guilt about sexual assertion with a woman surfaced and he was impotent.

His potency, however, returned shortly, and later on in the course of working with the sexual problem, he started a sexual affair, the details of which illustrate the need for him to defend against his guilt. He found someone he saw once a week for one hour solely for sexual relations. He was neither particularly attracted to her nor did he particularly like her. In questioning his motive for such an affair, I pointed out that what motivates most people to have an affair is attraction and sexual excitement, but that he goes from a wife who is not exciting enough to a mistress who is not exciting enough, so I couldn't see what he gained from this move. This led to further exploration of his guilt about sexual assertiveness, which he defended against by avoiding opportunities for excitement with either his wife or the other woman.

A Borderline Patient with Distancing Defenses

A 40-year-old woman with a borderline disorder of the self who was working at a job below her capacity described her love relationships as follows: She would get a telegram from Johannesburg, South Africa, from a man who was planning to visit New York for a week. He would arrive, they would engage in an intense round of romantic dinners, shows, drinking, and sex, and she would feel that he was in love with her. He would disappear, and after an interval, another man would come under similar circumstances and the same process would be repeated. In the meantime, no man ever appeared on the streets of New York. I finally asked her to clarify this for me by saying: "I wonder if you could help me clarify this? It seems to me that for a man to qualify for your bed he has to come by plane. I wonder why this is?" This led the patient to control the distancing defense and a man appeared on the streets of New York attempting to establish a relationship and she almost dissolved in separation anxiety.

Narcissistic Disorders of the Self—Problems with Intimacy

The inflated false self causes enormous problems with intimacy. In fact, narcissism and intimacy problems are practically synonymous. The exhibitionistic narcissist is unable to relate to other people except in terms of his or her own inflated self-image and unrealistic projections of himself or herself onto others. Every relationship involving a narcissistic personality requires adulation and perfect responsiveness from the partner or an idealization of the partner so that the narcissist can bask in the other's glow. Whenever these requirements are frustrated, or appear to be lacking from the narcissist's point of view, he or she experiences a lack of empathy and projects this onto the partner. And he or she devalues the partner, since the partner is not living up to the narcissist's wishes. The narcissist's overblown sense of entitlement makes it almost impossible for him or her to see what he or she is doing in these situations because the narcissist cannot imagine that his or her own projections onto the partner are causing such severe dissatisfaction in the relationship. He or she feels entitled to the narcissistic supplies and automatically responds with rage and devaluation of others when he or she doesn't get them. The narcissist's ability to appear charming and sensitive to others acts like a Venus flytrap for the unsuspecting lover, who can often be at a loss as to how to extricate herself or himself from the tangle of rage and blame that results from narcissistic disappointment.

The more reinforcement that life provides the narcissist in terms of success, money, power, or prestige, the more the narcissistic personality feels entitled to a mate who will provide the same. This may be one of the reasons why the divorce rate is exceptionally high among people with wealth and power; they grow so accustomed to getting what they want from others in life that they expect the same in their close relationships.

The most common arrangement is the narcissistic husband whose clinging borderline wife idealizes him and uses his sense of superiority to shore up her own inadequate self. She is usually very compliant, subservient, and eager to give him what he wants, but she always fails to meet his standards. Then her husband turns on her, attacks her for her inadequacies, and in so doing reinforces her negative feelings about herself. It is often only in treatment that she realizes how little she is getting out of the relationship.

A Man with Closet Narcissistic Defenses

A 33-year-old single, successful, professional man.

Chief Complaint: "I have no sense of self-worth—I'm not able to be as assertive as I would like to be—too ready to please others—don't do what I want—am not my own person—no passion for anything—tend to be tired and depressed—I'm afraid to commit myself to a relationship with a woman—I maintain a number of relationships and when intimacy threatens, I back off."

He has two women friends. He lived with a 27-year-old woman for seven years while having affairs on the side. He described her as warm and loving but very passive, childlike, and boring. The second, 33, a fellow professional, he has seen for one year. In contrast, he finds her exciting—more of a peer—but she is insisting on marriage. He reported: "I have no room left to maneuver—I've got to be more honest—I find marriage extremely frightening—the woman might change and I would be stuck—I have no confidence that a woman would change her life and if she does, it makes me very anxious—I tend to be attracted to hangers-on because they are easier to acquire, and it takes less energy to get what you want."

Past History: Father was an alcoholic who took little interest but nevertheless seemed to enjoy life without responsibility. His mother, on the other hand, was bitter, depressed, with no sense of self, demanding, intrusive, lived an extremely isolated and alienated life. He felt totally enclosed by her and he had to comply with her completely. Within the frame of this compliance, until age 9 he had felt a tremendous sense of self—special and unique—better than anyone—a superstar—precocious in school. He wanted to be a part of everything. However, around this time, "I realized I wasn't the superstar that others were. There were better students, better athletes, and I retreated from engagement to protect the image of myself as superstar. Then as a teenager I rebelled—started to take drugs and left home."

A Man with Exhibitionistic Defenses

A 53-year-old professional man, married with three children, the last of whom is a 13-year-old daughter.

Chief Complaint: A family problem with the daughter.

History of Present Illness: Both his wife and daughter report the father's angry outbursts and irritability at home that tend to focus on the daughter. "She's the problem." On closer examination, it seems that both the father and the mother are using the daughter as a vehicle to act out their conflict.

In the last two years, the father's business has been in great turmoil, with much loss of long-standing status and structure. He battled that out fairly successfully but got more angry, depressed, and disappointed in both his wife's and his daughter's ostensible lack of support. He attacked them, denying any depression. Nevertheless, he had great difficulty sleeping and was 50 pounds overweight.

The problem with intimacy was revealed by the wife, who reported that on the surface both partners were active, with productive and busy lives, but underneath the relationship had deteriorated as she gradually withdrew from his lack of sexual interest and his constant need to be special and admired. Five years earlier she had begun resuming professional work to take her out of the home.

The patient finally reported his lack of sexual interest for many years and emphasized his difficulty with intimacy as follows: "I was an only child—my mother was overwhelming and intrusive but it didn't seem to bother me, and I confided only in her and was quite open as a child. Throughout childhood and early adolescence, I felt quite special, unique, and admired so I didn't make much effort in school.

"When I was around 15 or 16 I could no longer stand my relationship with my mother. She couldn't accommodate my getting older—I had to separate and cut off. I did so, and at the same time I threw myself into school in order to become an outstanding student and then an outstanding professional. I have felt distant in relationships ever since.

"I hold back—I expect people to come to me but I am not welcoming when they do. With my mother I was a superchild, I did not have to work for it, and I relied on my wife to fill the gap. I am disappointed, hurt, and angry that she's withdrawn from me. She's busier than ever and seems more interested in our daughter. I can't tell her. My daughter is the problem because she is demanding closeness at a time when I need distance."

A Woman with a Closet Narcissistic Disorder Fuses with and Distances From an Idealized Object to Maintain Sense of Self

A 29-year-old woman, a painter.

Chief Complaint: Conflict in the marriage and inability to let go. She has been married for six years after she and her husband had lived together for one year, but two years ago, she began having an affair with a coworker. Two months prior to coming to see me she told her husband that she was going to leave him.

The husband, a businessman, 32, she described as having two sides. The side of him that reinforced her fusion fantasies was as follows: "We are too close, like Siamese twins. I felt like a baby, warm and safe and comfortable, I felt wrapped in cotton wool, but alienated from reality. I confused his body with my own—was more concerned about his psyche than my own."

She described his other side as follows: He was self-absorbed, obsessed with money, stingy, could not communicate emotion, had sexual difficulties—but she was terrified that he would leave her.

She described her fragmented self as follows: as "feeling hurt, wounded, exquisitely hypersensitive, almost having no skin, permeable to everybody and everything, terrified that my husband would disappear."

She described her lover as an artist in his mid-40s, who was also having a relationship with another woman at the same time.

Past History: Her mother had an exhibitionistic narcissistic disorder and turned her over to a governess at birth. The mother was hostile, sadistic, attacked all self-expression, and required her to mirror and comply with her expectations. Her father was an alcoholic who died when she was 3. The principal saving grace was a close relationship with a governess who was a mother surrogate until age 6. She managed in school and college, spending much of her time alone and absorbed in her painting. However, when she went to college, she had a severe depression for four years until she met her husband.

Diagnostic impression was a patient with a closet narcissistic disorder who required fusion and distancing defenses to maintain a sense of self. I began psychotherapy once a week to slowly evaluate her capacity to manage and deal with the inevitable disappointment, vulnerability, and exposure that would be associated with the frustration of her fusion fantasies in treatment.

I made a mirroring interpretation of her narcissistic vulnerability: It was so painful for her to focus on herself that she soothed that pain by focusing on her husband and others. She internalized these interpretations, began to activate her real self. She left the lover. She was activating her real self in her daily life, managing the recurrent narcissistic disappointment in the interviews, and was now being seen three times a week.

At this point, she decided that she must divorce her husband. She told him but then had a panic dream about being abandoned with the loss of self, which she then defended against by emotional distancing and detachment. She reported about the husband, "I'm either terrified or cut off at separating—I'm strangled by being with him."

At this point, I was going on vacation. She reported, "I had a fantasy of your dying on the trip and I shut off all feelings, but I'm now beginning to sense a pattern where before I felt the victim of chaos. I'm amazed at how I have to cut off all feelings with people, but I am still able to paint." She elaborated on her narcissistic vulnerability of self by saying, "I have no feelings with you, or anyone else unless they totally endorse me; otherwise I'm hurt. I panic and cut off. I can't handle closeness without distance but also can't stand to be distant."

During the course of this working through, she managed to do a substantial amount of successful painting. She reported her transference fantasies: "I have fantasies of merging with you, of being taken care of, of disappearing into your body like a wave of suction, I'd float in and disappear. At the same time, I realize I can play this out here where I am safe."

These fantasies were interpreted as defenses against her narcissistic vulnerability but she then turned to acting out these defenses. At this point, a man entered the scene—15 years older, vastly successful, physically huge—with an enormous charisma and social position. He had been married once in his 20s and then divorced, and had had no enduring relationships since. He was a workaholic who was extremely socially isolated. He pursued her avidly—told her how much he loved her—wanted to marry her—but the relationship was conditioned by several elements: First, distance. His work took him away for 12 weeks at a time, several times a year. Second, she was required to forego herself and cater to him. He was powerfully verbal and seductive. He promoted her symbiotic fantasies and she wished to disappear inside him so her self-activation was minimized.

This lasted about a year. Typical of the distancing defense, they kept their two apartments, which required her to commute back and forth. He avoided her efforts to get him to make a permanent commitment until she finally stood her ground. She couldn't go on this way. Overnight, literally overnight, as his fear of engulfment emerged, he told her he could not go on—he could not handle the closeness. She dealt with the feeling of loss by detaching and withdrawing. Interpretation and confrontation of her acting out fell on deaf ears.

About nine months later, a fourth man entered the scene. He was four or five years older—a professional, single, extremely affectionate, responsible, and very supportive of her. There was no distance in the relationship, because he worked in New York City. She liked him, was attracted to him, but felt there was something missing—that he was not a strong enough person. However, she wondered if his being around constantly was what was really bothering her, because she needed distance in order to be able to maintain a sense of self. "I'm either trembling with anxiety that he will reject me or I am constantly monitoring him or I am mad at him for not being more—continuity with him bothers me because I have a need to withdraw, to be alone and detached. Don't know which of these states is real or if either is real. Is he not right for me or does his being right for me frustrate my symbiotic wishes and stimulate my fear of loss of self so that I can't see him as he is? He acknowledges and supports my self so I can't bury and lose it in him and it makes merger fantasies unworkable. I can't seem to sustain my self with another person."

A Closet Narcissistic Disorder of the Self

Ms. A., tall, slender, blonde, a 40-year-old homosexual woman, was a successful interior decorator and the divorced mother of two children. She complained of difficulties in interpersonal relationships.

History of Present Illness: The patient had had her first homosexual relationship while in college. Later, she fell in love with a man, married, and in so doing lost her sense of self. She became "all things to her husband and children." She was married for 10 years, during which time there were no homosexual relationships.

She reported: "After 10 years, I realized I had no self, nor did I have any intimacy with my husband. I started to drink; I had a low tolerance for alcohol and became an alcoholic. I had blackouts. I drank for three years until last year, when I joined AA and started an affair with a woman. During the three years that I was drinking, I had three relationships: two with women and one with a man. All of the relationships were difficult and conflictual. I tended to sell out to women who were attracted to me.

"I then met another woman, an older woman who reminds me somewhat of my mother, and I have been having a relationship with her for the past year. I find her very distant. I find myself giving and then pulling back, and we have a lot of conflict.

"I have great difficulty acknowledging myself. I feel I have no self. I have trouble asserting myself. On the other hand, I have this idea that I can get away with anything. At one point I took Prozac but put on 35 pounds."

Personal History: "Mother was domineering, paranoid, with a will of iron, angry, attacking, stingy, a monster who never let me alone. Mother was also a very successful career woman. Father was a rather inadequate, kind, and distant man who was never available and who did not help me with my mother."

The patient was the oldest of three children, with sisters five years younger and seven years younger. She had to take care of the sisters, who also had serious problems in relationships.

"I was a latchkey kid, and at one point my mother took me to a psychologist, although I don't remember why."

Schizoid Disorders of the Self

The Case of George S.

A 47-year old businessman, currently separated from his wife of 20 years. The relationship has been on and off over all those years with many separations, one lasting for almost five years.

Marriage: About his marriage, George S. said, "I need a certain distance, and Ann [his wife] needs a certain closeness. The closeness makes me feel unsafe and I distance. She says that the distance makes her feel unsafe, and so she clings." (I think this is a beautiful description in one sentence of the differing relational conflicts between the schizoid and the borderline patient.)

Reflecting on this pattern, the patient commented, "It sure as hell is difficult to cut the cord. On the one hand, I feel like I want a connection, a family. But this always feels suffocating, as if I must accommodate totally. And I feel trapped. On the other hand, when I am by myself there are none of these bad feelings. But being unconnected can feel bad, as if I am worthless, devoid of a function. I guess that my dilemma is that I have a deep need for a connection and an equally deep need for separation and privacy." The patient felt that these themes have been present all his life.

"I have always had a problem committing to people." But not to things. He was always quite independent and successful in his professional life. His responsibility and obligation to his work, whether in school, college, or his profession, were never at issue. He could be as involved as needed, without ever feeling unsafe. However, "in most relationships, I require a certain distance."

Early History: He wondered whether it went back to his relationships growing up. He reflected that his parents were good people, yet they were always "at wit's end." He felt that they just could not be bothered with him. "I knew I really couldn't count on them emotionally. Home was never a safe harbor, and I had to distance myself. I want a connection, but I don't want to be in prison. I have a connection thing, I want a feeling of being connected, but not at the cost of enslavement. There is a signal when I get too close. I stop wanting to have sex. It becomes dangerous. I don't trust easily about my feelings. When I get close, I begin to feel that you are trying to manipulate me for your own purposes. It feels like you are trying to pry me open and in order to feel safe I must stay apart."

Conclusion

These examples illustrate the need for the therapist to decode the patient's illusions that the relationship works, identify the patient's defenses against abandonment or engulfment and bring them to the patient's attention through confrontation or interpretation so they can be worked through in therapy.

Contributors

Margot T. Beattie, Ph.D. Clinical Psychology, California School of Professional Psychology, 1987. Graduate Masterson Institute, 1994. Psychologist, Kaiser Medical Center, San Francisco, 1988–present; Director Neuropsychology Service, Kaiser Permanente Medical Center, 1990–1997; faculty, Masterson Institute, 1997; Program Director, Masterson Institute, West Coast Division, 1999.

Elinor Greenberg, Ph.D. Degree in psychology, New School for Social Research: Graduate Masterson Institute. Faculty member and supervisor, Masterson Institute (New York); also on the faculty of the New York Institute for Gestalt Therapy and adjunct faculty to the Gestalt Center for Psychotherapy and Training and the Gestalt Center of Long Island.

Arlene Hahn, M.S.W. Degree in social work, Yeshiva University. Graduate Masterson Institute. Faculty member, Masterson Institute, 1999. Faculty member in the Department of Community and Preventive Medicine, Mount Sinai School of Medicine.

Barbara L. Short, Ph.D. Degree in community psychology, University of California, San Francisco. Fellow and Diplomate of the American Board of Medical Psychologists. Graduate Masterson Institute (San Francisco) and a member of the faculty since 1997.

References

Chapter One

1.1. Ainsworth, M. D. S., Blehar, M., Waters, E., & Wall, S. (1978). *Patterns of attachment.* Hillsdale, NJ: Erlbaum.

1.2. Bates, J. E., Maslin, C. A., & Frankel, K. A. (1985). Attachment security, mother–child interaction and temperament as predictors of behavioral problem ratings at age three years. In I. Bretherton & E. Waters (Eds.), *Growing points of attachment theory and research.* Monographs of the Society for Research in Child Development, *50*(1–2, Serial No. 209), 167–193.

1.3. Bowlby, J. (1969). *Attachment and loss: Vol. 1. Attachment.* (1973). *Vol. 2. Separation: anxiety and anger.* (1980). *Vol. 3. Loss: Sadness and depression.* New York: Basic Books.

1.4. Brazelton, T. B. (1980, May). New knowledge about the infant from current research: Implications for psychoanalysis. Presented at the American Psychoanalytic Association meeting, San Francisco, Calif.

1.5. Brazelton, T. B. (1982). Joint regulation of neonate-parent behavior. In E. Tronick (Ed.), *Social interchange in infancy.* Baltimore: University Park Press.

1.6. Carlson, V., Cicchetti, D., Barnett, D., & Braunwald, K. G. (1989). Finding order in disorganization: Lessons from research on maltreated infants' attachments to their caregivers. In D. Cicchetti & V. Carlson (Eds.), *Child maltreatment: Theory and research on the causes and consequences of maltreatment* (pp. 494–526). New York: Cambridge University Press.

1.7. Emde, R. N., Klingman, D. H., Reich, J. H., & Wade, J. D. (1978). Emotional expression in infancy: I. Initial studies of social signaling and an emergent model. In M. Lewis & L. Rosenblum (Eds.), *The development of affect.* New York: Plenum Press.

1.8. Emde, R. N., & Sorce, J. E. (1983). The rewards of infancy: Emotional availability and maternal referencing. In J. D. Call, E. Galenson, & R. Tyson (Eds.), *Frontiers of infant psychiatry, Vol 2.* New York: Basic Books.

1.9. Erickson, M., Sroufe, L. A., & Egeland, B. (1985). The relationship between quality of attachment and behavior problems in preschool in a high-risk sample. In I. Bretherton & E. Waters (Eds.), *Growing points of attachment theory and research*. Monographs of the Society for Research in Child Development. *50*(1–2, Serial No. 209), 147–166.

1.10. Escalona, S. K. (1953). Emotional development in the first year of life. In M. Senn (Ed.), *Problems in infancy and childhood*. Packawack Lake, NJ: Foundation Press.

1.11. Heinicke, C., & Westheimer, I. (1966). *Brief separations*. New York: International Universities Press. London: Longmans Green.

1.12. Hinde, R. A. (1966). *Animal behaviour: A synthesis of ethology and comparative psychology*. New York: McGraw-Hill.

1.13. Lyons-Ruth, K. (1989, February). From birth to five: Development pathways of the young child at social risk. Address to the Bunting Institute Colloquium Series, Radcliffe College, Cambridge, Mass.

1.14. Lyons-Ruth, K. (1991). Rapprochement or approchement: Mahler's theory reconsidered from the vantage point of recent research on early attachment relationships. *Psychoanalytic Psychology, 8*(1), 1–23.

1.15. Lyons-Ruth, K., Connell, D. B., Grunebaum, H., & Botein, S. (1990). Infants at social risk: Maternal depression and family support services as mediators in infant development and security of attachment. *Child Development, 61*, 85–98.

1.16. Lyons-Ruth, K., Connell, D., Zoll, D., & Stahl, J. (1987). Infants at social risk: Relations among infant maltreatment, maternal behavior, and infant attachment behavior. *Developmental Psychology, 23*(2), 223–232.

1.17. Mahler, M. S., Pine, F., & Bergman, A. (1975). *The psychological birth of the human infant—symbiosis and individuation.* New York: Basic Books.

1.18. Mahler, M. S. (1965). An early infantile psychosis: The symbiotic and autistic syndromes. *Journal of the American Academy of Child Psychiatry, 4*, 554–568.

1.19. Mahler, M. S., & Gosliner, B. J. (1995). On symbiotic child psychosis: Genetic, dynamic and restitutive aspects. In *The psychoanalytic study of the child,* Vol. 10 (pp. 195–212). New York: International Universities Press.

1.20. Mahler, M. S. (1968). *On human symbiosis and the vicissitudes of individuation*, Vol. 1, *Infantile psychosis*. New York: International Universities Press.

1.21. Mahler, M. S. (1971). A study of the separation–individuation process and its possible application to borderline phenomena in the psychoanalytic situation. In *The psychoanalytic study of the child*, Vol. 26 (pp. 403–424). New York: Quadrangle.

1.22. Mahler, M. S. (1972a). On the first three subphases of the separation–individuation process. *International Journal of Psychoanalysis, 53*, 333–338.

1.23. Mahler, M. S. (1972b). Rapprochement subphase of the separation–individuation process. *Psychoanalytic Quarterly, 41*, 487–506.

1.24. Mahler, M. S. (1963a). Certain aspects of the separation–individuation phase. *Psychoanalytic Quarterly, 32*, 1–14.

1.25. Mahler, M. S. (1963b). Description of the subphases, history of the separation–individuation study, presented at Workshop IV: Research in Progress, American Psychoanalytic Association annual meeting, St. Louis, Mo., May 4, 1963, unpublished.

1.26. Main, M., & Hesse, E. (1990). Parents' unresolved traumatic experiences are related to infant disorganized attachment status: Is frightened and/or frightening parental behavior the linking mechanism? In M. Greenberg, D. Cicchetti, & E. M. Cummings (Eds.), *Attachment in the preschool years: Theory, research and intervention* (pp. 161–184). Chicago: University of Chicago Press.

1.27. Main, M., & Solomon, J. (1990). Procedures for identifying infants as disorganized/disoriented during the Ainsworth strange situation. In M. Greenberg, D. Cicchetti, & E. M. Cummings (Eds.), *Attachment in the preschool years: Theory, research and intervention* (pp. 121–160). Chicago: University of Chicago Press.

1.28. Main, M., & Weston, D. (1982). Avoidance of the attachment figure in infancy: Description and interpretation. In C. M. Parkes & J. Stevenson-Hinde (Eds.), *The place of attachment in human behavior* (pp. 203–217). London: Tavistock.

1.29. Masterson, J. (1972). *Treatment of the borderline adolescent: A developmental approach*. New York: Wiley.

1.30. Matas, L., Arend, R. A., & Stoufe, L. A. (1978). Continuity of adaptation in the second year: The relationship between quality of attachment and later competence. *Child Development, 49*, 547–556.

1.31. McDevitt, J. (1997). The continuity of conflict. *Journal of the American Psychoanalytic Association, 45*(1), 1997.

1.32. Robertson, J. (1953). Some responses of young children to loss of maternal care. *Nursing Times, 49*, 382–386.

1.33. Sander, L. W. (1962). Issues in early mother–child interaction. *Journal of the American Academy of Child Psychiatry, 1*, 141–166.

1.34. Sander, L. W. (1964). Adaptive relationships in early mother–child interaction. *Journal of the American Academy of Child Psychiatry, 3*, 231–264.

1.35. Sander, L. W. (1969). The longitudinal course of early mother–child interaction: Cross-case comparison in a sample of mother–child pairs. In B. M. Foss (Ed.), *Determinants of infant behaviour, Vol. 4*. London, New York: Barnes & Noble.

1.36. Schore, A. N. (1994). *Affect regulation and the origin of the self*. Hillsdale, NJ: Erlbaum.

1.37. Small, M. F. (1997). Our babies, ourselves. *Natural History Magazine*, Oct.

1.38. Spitz, R. A. (1965). *The first year of life*. New York: International Universities Press.

1.39. Stern, D. N. (1985). *The interpersonal world of the infant—a view from psychoanalysis and developmental psychology*. New York: Basic Books.
1.40. Thomas, A., Chess, S., & Birch, H. (1968). *Temperament and behavior disorders in children.* New York: New York University Press.

Chapter 2

2.1. Abend, S. M., Porder, M. S., & Willick, M. S. (1983). *Borderline patients: Psychoanalytic perspectives.* New York International Universities Press.
2.2. Adler, G., & Buie, D. H. (1979). Aloneness and borderline psychopathology, the possible relevance of child development issues. *International Journal of Psychoanalysis, 60,* 83.
2.3. Adler, G. (1985). *Borderline psychopathology and its treatment.* New York: Jason Aronson.
2.4. Ainsworth, M. D. S., Blehar, M., Waters, E., & Wall, S. (1978). *Patterns of attachment.* Hillsdale, NJ: Erlbaum.
2.5. Bowlby, J. (1980). *Attachment and loss: Vol. III, Loss, sadness and depression.* New York: Basic Books.
2.6. Boyer, L. B. (1983). *The regressed patient.* New York: Jason Aronson.
2.7. Brazelton, T. B. (1982). Joint regulation of neonate–parent behavior. In E. Tronic (Ed.), *Social interchange in infancy*. Baltimore: University Park Press.
2.8. Emde, R. N., Klingman, D. H., Reich, J. H., & Way, J. D. (1978). Emotional expression in infancy. In M. Lewis & L. Rosenblum (Eds.), *The development of affect.* New York: Plenium Press.
2.9. Fairbairn, W. R. D. (1954). *A revised psychopathology of the psychoses and psychoneuroses in psychoanalytic structures of the personality (an object relations theory of the personality*). London: Tavistock. New York: Basic Books,
2.10. Gabbard, G. O., et al. (1996). *The borderline personality disorder: Tailoring the psychotherapy to the patient.* Washington, DC: American Psychiatric Press.
2.11. Giovacchini, P. L. (1973). Character disorders: With special reference to the borderline state. *International Journal of Psychoanalytical Therapy,* 2, 7–36.
2.12. Goldstein, W. (1985). *An introduction to borderline conditions.* New York: Jason Aronson.
2.13. Gunderson, J., M.D. (1996). The borderline patient's intolerance of aloneness, insecure attachments and therapist's availability. *American Journal of Psychiatry*, June.
2.14. Kernberg, O. F. (1967). Borderline personality organization. *Journal of the American Psychoanalytic Association, 15*, 641–685.
2.15. Kernberg, O. F. (1968). Treatment of patients with borderline personality organization. *International Journal of Psychoanalysis, 49,* 600–619.

2.16. Kernberg, O. F. (1975). *Borderline conditions and pathological narcissism.* New York: Jason Aronson.

2.17. Klein, M. (1975). *Envy and gratitude and other works, 1946–1963.* New York: Delacorte.

2.18. Klein, M. (1948). *A contribution to the psychogenesis of manic depressive states.* In M. Klein (Ed.), *Contributions to psychoanalysis (1921, 1945).* London: Hogarth Press.

2.19. Kohut, H. (1977). *Restoration of the self.* New York: International Universities Press.

2.20. Kohut, H. (1971). *The analysis of the self.* New York: International Universities Press.

2.21. Linehan, M. M. (1996). Dialectical behavior therapy (DBT) for borderline personality disorder. *Journal of California Alliance for the Mentally III, 8*(1), 44–46.

2.22. Lyons-Ruth, K. (1991). Rapprochement or approchement: Mahler's theory reconsidered from the vantage point of recent research on early attachment relationships. *Psychoanalytic Psychology, 8*(1), 1–23.

2.23. Mahler, M. S., Pine, F., & Bergman, A. (1975). *The psychological birth of the human infant, symbiosis and individuation.* New York: Basic Books.

2.24. Masterson, J. F. (1968). The psychiatric significance of adolescent turmoil. *American Journal of Psychiatry, 124*(11), 107–112.

2.25. Masterson, J. F. (1972). *Psychiatric dilemma of adolescence* (in Spanish). Buenos Aires: PAIDOS-ASAPPIA.

2.26. Masterson, J. F. (1973). The tie that binds: Maternal clinging, separation–individuation and the borderline syndrome. *International Journal of Child Psychotherapy*, 2, 331–344.

2.27. Masterson, J. F., & Rinsely, D. B. (1975). The borderline syndrome: The role of the mother in the genesis and psychic structure of the borderline personality. *International Journal of Psychiatry, 56*, 163–178.

2.28. Masterson, J. F. (1976). *Psychotherapy of the borderline adult: A developmental approach.* New York: Brunner/Mazel.

2.29. Masterson, J. F. (1978). The borderline adult: Therapeutic alliance and transference. *American Journal of Psychiatry, 135*(4), 437–441.

2.30. Masterson, J. F. (Ed.) (1978). *New perspectives on psychotherapy of the borderline adult, J. F. Masterson, P. L. Giovacchini, H. F. Searles, O. F. Kernberg, M.D.'s.* New York: Brunner/Mazel.

2.31. Masterson, J. F. (1980). *The test of time: Borderline adolescent to functioning adult, A follow-up report of psychoanalytic psychotherapy of the borderline adolescent and family.* New York: Brunner/Mazel.

2.32. Masterson, J. F. (1980). The borderline syndrome: The role of the mother in the genesis and psychic structure of the borderline personality: In R. F. Lax, S. Bach, & J. A. Burland (Eds.), *Rapprochment: The critical subphase of separation-individualtion.* New York: Jason Aronson.

2.33. Masterson, J. F. (1981). *Narcissistic and borderline disorders: An integrated developmental approach.* New York: Brunner/Mazel.
2.34. Masterson, J. F. (1985). *The real self. A developmental, self, and object relations approach.* New York: Brunner/Mazel.
2.35. Masterson, J. F. (1985). *Treatment of the borderline adolescent: A developmental approach* (2nd ed.). New York: Brunner/Mazel.
2.36. Masterson, J. F. (1988). *The search for the real self—unmasking the personality disorders of our age.* New York: Free Press.
2.37. Masterson, J. F. (1993). *The emerging self—a developmental, self, and object relations approach to the treatment of the closet narcissistic disorder of the self.* New York: Brunner/Mazel.
2.38. Meissner, W. W. (1984). *The borderline spectrum, differential diagnosis and developmental issues.* New York: Jason Aronson.
2.39. Meissner, W. W. (1988). *Treatment of patients in the borderline spectrum.* New York: Jason Aronson.
2.40. Oldham, J. M. (1996). Borderline personality disorder: The treatment dilemma. *Journal of California Alliance for the Mentally Ill, 8*(1), 13–15.
2.41. Paris, J. (1996). Borderline personality disorder: What is it? What causes it? How can we treat it? *Journal of California Alliance for the Mentally Ill, 8*(8), 5–6.
2.42. Rosenfeld, H. (1978). Notes on the psychopathology and psychoanalytic treatment of some borderline patients. *International Journal of Psychoanalysis, 59,* 215–221.
2.43. Schacter, D. L. (1996). *Searching for memory; The brain, the mind and the past.* New York: Basic Books.
2.44. Schore, A. *The role of affect in the emergence of the self.* Hillsdale, NJ: Erlbaum.
2.45. Siever, L. J. (1996). The biology of borderline personality disorder. *Journal of California Alliance for the Mentally Ill, 8*(1), 18–19.
2.46. Stern, D. N. (1985). *The interpersonal world of infant—a view from psychoanalysis and developmental psychology.* New York: Basic Books.
2.47. Trestment, R. L. (1996). The challenge of borderline personality disorder. *Journal of California Alliance for the Mentally Ill, 8*(1), 11–13.
2.48. Vela, R. M. (1996). Borderline personality disorder: Is it possible in children under twelve? *Journal of California Alliance for the Mentally Ill, 8*(1).
2.49. Zoloft, T. H. (1987). Neuroleptic treatment in the borderline patient: Advantages and techniques. *Journal of Clinical Psychiatry, 48* (supplement) (8), 26–30.

Chapter 3

3.1. Erikson, E. (1968). *Identity, youth, and crisis* (pp. 208–231). New York: Norton.

3.2. Masterson, J. F. (1985). *The real self: A developmental, self, and object relations approach*. New York: Brunner/Mazel.
3.3. Westen, D., & Arkowitz-Westen, L. (1998). Limitation of Axis II in diagnosing personality in clinical practice. *American Journal of Psychiatry, 155*, 12.
3.4 Winnicott, D. (1965). *Ego distortions in terms of true and false self in the maturational processes and the facilitation environment* (pp. 140–152). New York: International Universities Press.

Chapter 4

4.1. Gunderson, J. M. D., & Phillips (1991). Literature of interface between borderline personality disorder and depression. *American Journal of Psychiatry*, Aug.
4.2. Samenow, S. E. (1998). *Straight talk about criminals*. Northvale, NJ: Jason Aronson.

Chapter 5

5.1. Fairbairn, W. R.-D. (1984). *Psychoanalytic studies of the personality* (p. 91). London: Routledge & Kegan Paul.
5.2. Masterson, J. F. (1981). *Narcissistic and borderline disorder: An integrated developmental approach*. New York: Brunner/Mazel.

Chapter 9

9.1. Mahler, M., Pine, F., & Bergman, A. (1975). *The psychological birth of the human infant: Symbiosis and individuation*. London: Hutchinson.
9.2. Stern, D. N. (1985). *The interpersonal world of the infant*. New York: Basic Books.
9.3. Wallerstein, J., & Kelly, J. B. (1990). *Surviving the breakup: How children and parents cope with a divorce*. New York: Basic Books.

Index